HEADING FOR THE SCOTTISH HILLS

Compiled by
the Mountaineering Council of Scotland
and
the Scottish Landowners' Federation

Published by
the Scottish Mountaineering Trust

First published in Great Britain in 1988 by the Scottish Mountaineering Trust

British Library Cataloguing in Publication Data.
Heading for the Scottish Hills.
    I.   Scotland. Highlands. Hill walking Manuals
    I.   Mountaineering Council of Scotland
    II.   Scottish Landowners' Federation 796.5'22
ISBN 0-907521-24-X

All the maps in this book are reproduced from Sheets 1, 2, 3, and 4 of the Ordnance Survey 1:250,000 Routemaster Series maps with the permission of the Controller of Her Majesty's Stationery Office. Crown copyright reserved

The Mountaineering Council of Scotland and the Scottish Landowners' Federation acknowledge the assistance of the Association of Deer Management Groups and of the Scottish Mountaineering Trust in the preparation and publication of this book.

Front cover: Heading up Glen Dochard towards Meall nan Eun (P Hodgkiss)
Back cover: Consultation on Rothiemurchus Estate (W McKenna)
Compilation: 1988/1989 Maureen Prior; 1993/1996 Dougal Roy
Maps reproduced by permission of the Ordnance Survey
Production by Scottish Mountaineering Trust (Publications) Ltd
Typesetting by John McKinlay, 11-15 King Street, Perth
Colour separations by Arneg, Glasgow
Printed by St. Edmundsbury Press, Bury St Edmunds
Bound by Hunter and Foulis, Edinburgh
Distributed by Cordee, 3a De Montfort Street, Leicester, LE1 7HD

CONTENTS

Scotland's Hills And Mountains: A Concordat on Access

Scotland's hills and mountains have great natural beauty; they are of high value for open-air recreation and of great importance for wildlife. They are in various forms of private and public ownership and are the home and workplace for sparse and economically fragile populations.

More people are visiting the hills and patterns of open-air recreation are changing. Recreation is now a major use of the hills alongside the traditional activities of hill farming, forestry, field sports and deer management. All are important providers of employment.

There is a common interest between all these land uses because they depend on the natural resources of the hills. There is also a common responsibility on all who visit and manage the hills to conserve wildlife and to have regard for the welfare of livestock.

The parties to the Concordat have come together because there is an urgent need for co-operation between the different users of hill land. The aim is to establish better understanding between the various interests in order to promote tolerance and to encourage co-operation.

There is a long standing tradition of access to hill land in Scotland - cherished by those who use the hills and long accepted by landowners and managers where this freedom is exercised with responsibility. As more people go to the hills, there is a growing need to encourage sensitive management and recreational practice. The Concordat aims to ensure that people can continue to enjoy access to the open hill in a way which shows consideration for the interests of others. The parties to the Concordat agree that the basis of access to the hills for informal recreation should be as follows:

- Freedom of access exercised with responsibility and subject to reasonable constraints for management and conservation purposes.

- Acceptance by visitors of the needs of land management, and understanding of how this sustains the livelihood, culture and community interests of those who live and work in the hills.

- Acceptance by land managers of the public's expectation of having access to the hills.

- Acknowledgement of a common interest in the natural beauty and special qualities of Scotland's hills, and of the need to work together for their protection and enhancement.

Making the Concordat Work

The success of the Concordat will depend on all who manage or visit the hills acting on the four principles set out here. In addition, the parties to the Concordat will promote good practice in the form of:

- Courtesy and consideration at a personal level.
- A welcome to visitors.
- Making advice readily available on the ground or in advance.
- Better information about the uplands and hill land uses through environmental education.
- Respect by visitors for the welfare needs of livestock and wildlife.
- Adherence to relevant codes and standards of good practice by visitors and land managers alike.
- Any local restrictions on access should be essential for the needs of management, should be fully explained, and be for the minimum period and area required.

Implementation

The Concordat has been agreed by all the parties represented on the Access Forum, which are:

- bodies representing farmers, managers and owners of hill land, where access takes place;
- voluntary bodies representing many different recreational activities which require access;
- and public bodies which have roles in promoting and facilitating enjoyment of open-air recreation.

The signatories agree to promote the general adoption of the principles set out above; to prepare and promote information and advice on the harmonisation of recreation with other land uses; to endeavour to resolve differences of opinion through discussion; and to keep under review the overall framework for the provision and management of access to Scotland's hills.

The signatories to this document will foster a caring and responsible approach to access, both by those who visit the hills for enjoyment and by those who own and manage Scotland's uplands. The public bodies acknowledge their role in assisting the implementation of the Concordat, including providing advice and helping to secure the resources necessary for the successful management of access.

The Concordat has been prepared and agreed by:

Association of Deer Management Groups
Convention of Scottish Local Authorities
Mountaineering Council of Scotland
National Farmers' Union of Scotland
Ramblers' Association Scotland

Scottish Countryside Activities Council
Scottish Landowners' Federation
Scottish Natural Heritage
Scottish Sports Association
Scottish Sports Council

FOREWORD

Magnus Magnusson KBE

Our hills and mountains are a national treasure. Their beauty provides Scotland's people and Scotland's visitors with spiritual refreshment and aesthetic pleasure, while their rugged qualities and harsh climate allow for adventure and challenge and, through this, self-discovery for the individual. But public enjoyment is only one of the uses to which we put our hills. Walkers and climbers share them with those who own and work the land - the hill farmers, the stalkers, the ghillies and the foresters. The sharing theme promoted through this guide is of vital importance, because it creates the framework for an approach of consideration and respect for other interests.

The Access Forum's *Concordat on Access to Scotland's Hills and Mountains* was an important watershed in the long and sometimes impassioned debate over access to the hills and mountains of Scotland. I am delighted to see that the Concordat is printed as a frontispiece to this edition of *Heading for the Scottish Hills*, and hope that everyone involved - providers, users and enablers - will embrace its principles and bring a new spirit of harmony to the hills.

All who use the hills also share them with their wildlife. Here live some very special plants and animals, which must command our respect for their ability to survive in some of the most difficult and also the most natural environments in the country. This very harshness limits their ability to recover naturally when disturbed or damaged. Thus plants on high and infertile land have a short growing season in which to flourish and seed, and any seedlings have a long severe winter through which to survive. In the same way, disturbance to animals which are under stress from the vagaries of the climate can have a critical impact on their well-being.

We are also becoming ever more aware of the international importance of some of these plant and animal communities, and European legislation is placing increasing responsibility on all of us to care for them better. At the same time, economic pressures on local land management are increasing, while more of us are wanting to use the hills for enjoyment. As a nation we are asking more of these special places and in turn this emphasises the need for more respect and more responsible sharing.

We also have a responsibility to protect the qualities of our uplands for future users. Thinking and acting for the long term is never easy, but we must be concerned to minimise our impacts and not to cause damage which is either not containable or eventually irreversible. Better still, we should be endeavouring to remedy past impacts in order to pass on an environment which is enhanced in its qualities. To achieve this we need understanding as well as commitment by all who care and use the hills - we need the Concordat in fact.

Understanding, sharing and respect all accord with the 'tread lightly' approach to the use of the hills, as promoted by the Mountaineering Council of Scotland. I wish the users of this guide safe and enjoyable days on the hill - and urge them all to remember to tread lightly.

INTRODUCTION

Graeme Gordon and Nick Kempe

This new edition is further evidence of co-operation between the Scottish Landowners' Federation and the Mountaineering Council of Scotland formally working together as they have done since 1972 in order to provide access information for those going to the hills, and to enable them to communicate and co-operate with those who work there.

Increased leisure time, improved communications, television programmes and the publication of numerous climbing books all contribute to attract an ever increasing number of people to the hills. At the same time, because of changing economic circumstances, some landowners may be restricted in the way they would like to manage their estates which generally employ fewer people today than hitherto.

The most significant development to have occurred since the publication of the last edition has been the launch of the Access Concordat - reprinted in full as a frontispiece. There is public acceptance of having access to the hills, but freedom of access has to be exercised with responsibility and the land manager, not unreasonably, expects the walker to respect, cherish and conserve the environment, its plants and wildlife, and to act reasonably. Contact should be made at critical times of the year and the visitor should be prepared to accept, on occasions, an alternative route in order to avoid disrupting the essential work of an estate. Landowners or their representatives for their part are also expected to provide information and an alternative route if at all possible while accepting traditional freedom of access at all other times.

This approach on both sides embodies in principle what the MCofS and SLF have been seeking to promote for some time through the publication of this book and, in this edition, we have tried to provide positive information in the estates' comments section. It is not possible, however, to impose a uniformed standard on every estate as needs differ.

Encouraging hillwalkers to telephone an estate number is not without its difficulties as telephones cannot always be manned, and answer phones have their limitations. The MCofS and SLF are currently exploring ways to improve the system and 1996 will see the launch, in conjunction with Scottish Natural Heritage, of experimental hill phones whereby one number will cover several estates in a number of areas. Hill signs and maps are another way to communicate, and we are working towards the production of signs that provide positive information within the spirit of the Access Concordat. We are also working on a number of educative items to encourage greater responsibility and co-operation, thereby enhancing the enjoyment of everyone who visits the Scottish hills.

Good walking and climbing.

THE WALKER'S VIEW

Rennie McOwan

The rewards for going to the Scottish hills are many and varied. Hills mean different things to different people, but there is an over all factor which is of the utmost importance.

The vast majority of hillwalkers and mountaineers believe they have a *right* to go to the mountain world in a responsible fashion, showing sensitivity and good manners towards the needs of hillfarms and estates. They regard access as a right and not a concession.

This belief is passionately held, has become part of the Scottish psyche for thousands of people and has been a continuously held tradition over many centuries. It is held as a moral right, as a right in folk tradition and - let us be clear - as a legal right in most instances and as expressed within the law of Scotland.

Most outdoor folk desire harmony in the hills. One of the best ways to ensure that is to be clear about the *facts*. There have been too many statements in recent years about access which are plainly wrong or out of focus and it is important that this static be removed.

Some individuals within Government departments and in the countryside establishment have said - and say - that mountaineers and hillwalkers go to the hills with the landowner's 'tacit consent' or with the owner's 'tolerance' (a legal expression).

This might well mean that public access is accepted by the owner and, therefore, provided good behaviour is present, there need be no hassle. However, that is not the complete picture.

If 'tacit consent' or 'tolerance' were to be removed tomorrow the boot traffic to the hills would continue as before. *That is reality.* It is not truculent, nor uncaring, to say that, merely to state the facts. The issue today, therefore, is one of sharing and two-way good sense.

It is also said that an owner has the right in law to ask a walker to leave and few (if any) lawyers would disagree with that. It is also said that an owner may use just sufficient force to achieve that object: this statement is promulgated frequently, but it is out-of-focus because many lawyers disagree with it. A very serious reason would have to be there for such an action to be acceptable and "I don't want you on the ground" is not sufficient.

Some tourist authorities have taken to saying that "walking is by permission". This is also untrue. Walking is *not* by permission. What is needed for the visitor is good advice about where to walk without harm, about where to consult and about how to behave responsibly and how to understand (and not harm) countryside needs in Scotland. There will be times, of course, and specific sites where to ask permission *is* a sensible courtesy *in that instance* and in case stock or privacy are harmed. But it is not needed in appropriate terrain and outwith specific dates.

The law is outlined elsewhere in this book, but it is not possible to assess Scots law accurately in relation to access without regard to folk tradition.

The mere fact of being on the ground in appropriate terrain, in so-called "wild land", is not, *of itself*, an offence. If no offence is being committed - say thousands - then nothing illegal is being done *in these circumstances*. If nothing illegal is being done, then the presence is 'legal'.

In saying this, it is important to stress that such attitudes are not pugnacious, nor are they a minority view. They are reality.

It is a mistake for some owners and planners to regard going to the hills as if it is like a round of golf or a game of darts. There is much of the spirit and the soul about it all, of a love of the mountain world, of freedom to wander and to change one's mind according to route and weather. It cannot readily be 'organised' or controlled according to rules, nor should it be.

We need an end, too, to mistakes in countryside documentation and an end to books published south of the Border which carry access material about England and Wales and state or imply that the same access history applies to Scotland. We can all learn from one another.

It is important that the modern hillwalker and mountaineer truly understands Scottish access history and its six main stages. It is sometimes erroneously said that so-called freedom-to-roam has a pedigree of about a century. That is a palpable nonsense.

Anyone who has made a study of Gaelic literature, of poetry, story, song, prayers, anecdotes, blessings, knows that in the centuries leading up to the 19th century sporting estates' legislation, that people, broadly speaking, walked where they liked in their glens and straths and on their hills.

We are *not* talking about the drove routes, the sheiling patterns, common grazing, and other factors which might nowadays be termed 'commercial'. These activities were often governed by laws or regulations of one kind or another. We *are* talking about activities which we would nowadays consider to be 'recreational', strolling, roaming, travelling on foot, relishing landscape, praising its beauty and a strong sense of possession.

All of this is plainly evident, yet too much Scottish access documentation in recent years has simply omitted or galloped over this period. There are hundreds of references to access being a normal part of the life of the people.

It was not formally set down in law, but it did not need to be. It was as natural as breathing or going for a swim.

Gaelic sources show an angry and bewildered people when their access was barred mainly in the 19th century. Even when 'trespass legislation' came into being there was a strong ground-swell of resentment and that, too, is recorded.

That great access campaigner, Viscount James Bryce, made it plain that he and thousands of others believed that the scenery of Scotland had been filched from the people. In no other country in the world, he said, were there such restrictions over uncultivated ground. It was not enough to have some path corridors. Traditional and general freedom-to-roam was being curtailed and he campaigned vigorously against restrictions. At the same time, some walkers and mountaineers simply carried on with *de facto* access.

In studying the Bills he placed before Parliament, and the ground work that led up to them, it should be noted that Bryce was supported by Scottish public opinion. Organisations or hobby groups, such as geologists or artists, joined forces with burghs and cities to produce petitions backing Bryce and wanting access formally protected in law. This period is worth detailed study because it gives the lie to those who say that 'access' is a recent development or that there was no national opinion.

Two world wars and changing social conditions altered the pattern. So did the burgeoning outdoor boom. Estates' staff changed and a kind of co-existence began to spring up, a kind of mutual tolerance. This can sound like an over-simplification, but broadly speaking, more and more owners accepted - or had to accept - public access and, more and more outdoor folk deepened their knowledge of farm needs. Badly behaved people were always in a minority both then and now.

There were spectacular blemishes on both sides, but there was a sea change.

The campaign to clarify legal rights of ways is a debate within the debate and as this contribution is about general access I will simply say that wider access made the right of way definition a secondary matter in many cases. Wider access *included* corridors.

Modern plans to create networks of paths in farm or urban land are excellent, but such paths are complementary to wider access when conditions make that appropriate and *not* substitutes for it.

My generation have inherited responsible freedom-to-roam. It has always been a fact in our lives. It is one of the reasons why people say - erroneously - that there is no law of trespass in Scotland. They say that because the *de facto* position is stronger than the *de jure* position.

Outdoor writers who concentrate solely on "access agreements", approved or 'official' paths and parks are guilty of poor research. Local Authorities and others who nowadays produce access strategy plans and manage to avoid mentioning the Scottish mainstream position and responsible freedom-to-roam are guilty of verbal gymnastics and startling omissions. It will no longer do.

We are talking about rights, about the right to responsible freedom-to-roam. An owner who accepts the public on the hills and a walker who feels he or she does not need that acceptance can, nevertheless, work together for the common good.

The modern scare about the new legislation of Aggravated Trespass being used against a *bona fide* walker has now been cleared up and the landowners' assurances that it is not intended to stop walkers and mountaineers are generally accepted. The outdoor organisations rightly stay on alert over the point, of course.

Freedom-to-roam is not a licence to misbehave. It means understanding the needs of farms and estates, of respecting stalking dates by changing routes or consulting over times and areas. It means being sensitive about calving, lambing, young forestry, crops and wild life. It means quiet and thoughtful behaviour.

Most of us treasure our friendships with stalkers, farmers, shepherds, factors and, yes, owners. Badly behaved mountaineers are the enemies of access.

We want countryside skills and manners to be as high in the mountaineer's list of capabilities as navigation or the correct use of ice-axe and crampons.

If there is two-way good sense, then co-existence works.

If co-existence breaks down then the owner comes off worst. That is a harsh fact, but it is reality. No responsible person wants hassle in the hills.

The Concordat is a brave attempt to go forward. Some see it as a way of stopping access legislation, others as a means of bringing about changes in the law. But if the end result is pleasing to both owner and walker/ climber, in that both have a workable pattern of access, then the scene is set fair, at least in the short term.

The much respected Patrick Gordon-Duff-Pennington, former Convener of the Scottish Landowners' Federation, said that if the day should come when the people of Scotland could no longer go to their mountains in a fitting fashion, then Scotland would have ceased to be Scotland.

The poet John Barbour said many centuries ago: "Ah, freedom is a noble thing. Freedom makes man to have *liking*". The word liking here, of course, means a dignified and responsible freedom.

All those who love the hills, who are possessed by them, have a very real sense of possession. But it brings responsibilities with it, to be guardians and protectors and carers.

We do not seek rights without responsibility. We recognise other people have rights.

But our hill freedom *is* a right, part of a long rope which goes back to Celtic times and which has experienced many strains and which has never been broken.

We hold it yet and will hand it on.

THE LANDOWNER'S VIEW

Patrick Gordon-Duff-Pennington

Landowners are no better and no worse than the rest of the population, but they have a contribution to make, based often on many generations' knowledge of the land. Whether they acquired their holdings by fair means or foul is ancient history, but inside most of their heads is a certain collective wisdom which it would be a mistake to discard under a guillotine in the streets of Inverness. All but a few can identify with the aspirations of mountaineers and hillwalkers, but a tiny apoplectic minority, seeking to guard their privilege and their privacy, still do huge damage to the cause of their fellow landowners. They should remember Grace Kelly's comment some time before she died "How I wish to be remembered is as a decent human being and a caring one!".

Those who come to the hills are mostly descendants of people who had to leave to make their living in the towns. The love of the hills - which they still regard as their hills - remains deep within them, and most are acutely conscious of the damage that careless access may cause to the land and to the livelihood of those few who still work in the high places. They will continue to come, mountaineers and hillwalkers, and they must be made to feel welcome in return for the courtesy which most of them show. The days of colonels with red faces and bad livers taking pot shots at the President of the Mountaineering Council of Scotland on the end of a rope on the Ardverikie Wall (for example!) after a bad day on the hill should remain securely in some ancient cartoon!

Landowners have a long tradition of stewardship. For them there is no escape from the old aboriginal saying: "We belong to the land; the land does not belong to us". Of course there are problems for landowners - how I dislike the word - in the management of the land. They feel that they have responsibility for the communities who rely on them for employment. Too often they see those who come contributing little or nothing to the economics of the area. They are bludgeoned by an ever-increasing amount of paper, imposing restrictions and regulations - and extra costs - on everything they do. Some have to work in Edinburgh, London or Glasgow to earn enough to maintain a house which is a listed building of doubtful significance, erected in the age of Britain's industrial wealth. They are blackguarded unjustly, sometimes by me, for being divorced from the changing realities of the turning season among the rocks, and from the aspirations of the communities for which they are still responsible.

From their responsibilities there is no escape, and when they cull the deer they are not happy if a line of brightly coloured cagoules, blissfully unaware of a changing wind and deer which they cannot see, scatters the animals into the blue yonder. Hillwalkers who have trodden the hills since early youth will understand the season may be late, the wind contrary. If, however, they have not been brought up in the hills, and are young, there is a mighty task of education and information to be undertaken. Much of the responsibility for this must lie with estates themselves, and it calls for all the imagination which landowners and factors can devise, as well as the help of Scottish Natural Heritage. With this in mind, the formation of Deer Management Groups, who now have their own Association, must be the most sensible way of co-operating for the foreseeable future - and guess what! Landowners are mostly loners who do not like co-operating!

If landowners do not belong, and do not know the name of the Secretary of the local group, they should contact the Secretary of the Association of Deer Management Groups.

If they will not belong they should examine their consciences, because the active participation of every landowner in the Red Deer range is vital for the welfare of the deer and the grouse moors in their charge. The cost of running a Highland estate is astronomical. By comparison the cost of belonging to a deer group, with its advantage of shared experience and shared aims, is tiny. Some groups already include representatives of other interested organisations in their meetings. The people who come need information, and although a vast number of notice boards would not be welcome to anybody, a minimum would be of considerable benefit. In most places they are still conspicuous by their absence. Apart from anything else this has safety implications which need addressing. No longer is it acceptable to erect boards with KEEP OUT. Many deer groups have a considerable expertise in designing suitable information boards which will help the enjoyment of the hills for everybody who comes.

Landowners know well that more people will come to the hills and some do not know how to face the problem. A few think they dislike hillwalkers and mountaineers because they see them unjustly as a threat to their sport, their privacy, and their economic privilege. They should remember how I joined up at Fort George and my platoon commander went one day to visit his father who had been Pipe Major of the 1st Seaforths. To him he said: "Father, I bloody well can't stick that man!", to which his father replied: "Well, my boy, perhaps it's just that you don't know him very well!". A wise man with the recipe for maintaining the spiritual qualities and inviolate nature of the hills which can mean so much. A recipe for peace.

It may not always be easy, but the plea to those who administer estates in the hills must be for toleration at all times. That way they will make many friends. Take the other road and they will shortly find they are an anachronism - a mere footnote on the page of Scottish history.

THE LAW RELATING TO ACCESS

Alan Page and Duncan Thomson

1. Introduction

Hillgoers do not enjoy a legally enforceable right of access to the Scottish hills. The often quoted "right to roam" may be understood to be a moral right but it is not a legal one. Freedom of access to the hills relies on the long-standing, common sense tradition of mutual tolerance between landowners and the public where access to open country is concerned.

2. Public Rights of Way

In some cases, for example, the Glen Tilt hills, access may involve the use of a public right of way. There are also some public paths established in the exercise of statutory powers which, like public rights of way, members of the public may use as a matter of right. For further information, see *Rights of Way: A Guide to the Law in Scotland*, published by the Scottish Rights of Way Society Ltd. in 1996.

3. Trespass

Where there is no public right of way or statutory equivalent, access depends on the consent of the landowner concerned. A person who goes on to land without the consent of the landowner is, in the eyes of the law, a trespasser. Trespass is not in itself a criminal offence, so no prosecution can follow; nor may damages be claimed unless actual damage has been caused. A trespasser may, however, be asked to leave and, if he refuses to go, reasonable force may be used to remove him. A Court Order may also be sought prohibiting a person who refuses to leave, or a persistent intruder, from future trespass.

4. Criminal Offences

Aggravated Trespass

Although trespass is not in itself a criminal offence, there are certain offences of which it is an ingredient, including the offence of Aggravated Trespass created by the Criminal Justice and Public Order Act 1994. Aggravated Trespass involves the *intentional* disruption, obstruction, or intimidation of persons engaged in lawful, open-air activity. Since hillgoers will normally lack the necessary intention, they cannot be convicted of the offence, even where, as may happen, they (unintentionally) disrupt lawful outdoor activity.

Camping

The Trespass (Scotland) Act 1865 makes it an offence to camp or light fires on private land without the consent of the landowner.

5. Access by Vehicle

The principles outlined in paragraphs 2 and 3 apply to access by car as well as to access on foot. In addition, the Road Traffic Act 1988 makes it an offence to drive on to private land without lawful authority. No offence is committed where a person drives within 15 yards of a public road for the purpose of parking. This does not mean that one has a right to park within 15 yards of a public road. It is also an offence to drive a motor vehicle on a footpath or cycle track.

6. Bicycles

Regular use of a particular route by cyclists for 20 years may create a public right of way, but it is otherwise an offence to ride a bicycle on a footpath in the absence of a specific right to do so. Cycling off a footpath is not an offence but is governed by the civil law of trespass.

7. Dogs

The Animals (Scotland) Act 1987 imposes strict liability, i.e. liability without proof of fault, in respect of injury or damage caused by dogs and certain other animals. The same legislation entitles a landowner to destroy a dog which is a threat to livestock. A person taking a dog into an area in which there is a risk of injury or harm being caused should therefore keep the dog on a lead or otherwise under his close control.

IMPORTANT TIMES OF THE YEAR FOR SOME COUNTRYSIDE ACTIVITIES

Red Deer Stalking: the open season for shooting red deer stags is from 1 July - 20 October, and for hinds from 21 October - 15 February. However, the most critical time is generally from mid-August to mid-October.

Lambing: the exact time of hill lambing in Scotland varies according to the area, but is generally between mid-April and the end of May. It is especially important to keep dogs on leads at this time.

Grouse Shooting: the grouse shooting season runs from 12 August to 10 December, with most shoots taking place during the earlier part of that period.

Ground nesting birds on moorland can be very vulnerable to disturbance, and walkers should therefore take particular care at nesting time, especially as regards dogs running free.

SOME USEFUL ADDRESSES

The Mountaineering Council of Scotland
4a St Catherine's Road, Perth   PH1 5SE
Tel: 01738 638227

The Scottish Landowners' Federation
25 Maritime Street, Edinburgh   EH6 5PW
Tel: 0131 555 1031

The Association of Deer Management Groups
Dalhousie Estates Office, Brechin, Angus DD9 9DL
Tel: 01356 624566 or 624567

The Scottish Rights of Way Society
John Cotton Business Centre, 10 Sunnyside, Edinburgh EH7 5RA
Tel: 0131 652 2937

Scottish Natural Heritage
12 Hope Terrace, Edinburgh EH9 2AS
Tel: 0131 447 4784

The Scottish Sports Council
Caledonia House, South Gyle, Edinburgh EH12 9DQ
Tel: 0131 317 7200

For mountain safety advice please see *The Scottish Mountain Code* compiled with
the assistance of the Mountaineering Council of Scotland and published by the
Scottish Sports Council.

AREAS COVERED BY MAPS

The estate boundaries shown on the maps are for area identification only, and are not intended to indicate legal accuracy.

This symbol ▲, in red, denotes a camp site.

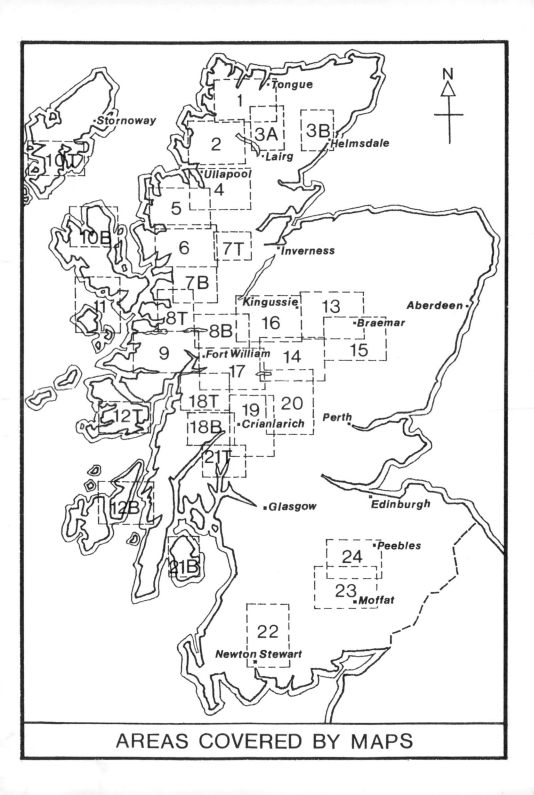

AREAS COVERED BY MAPS

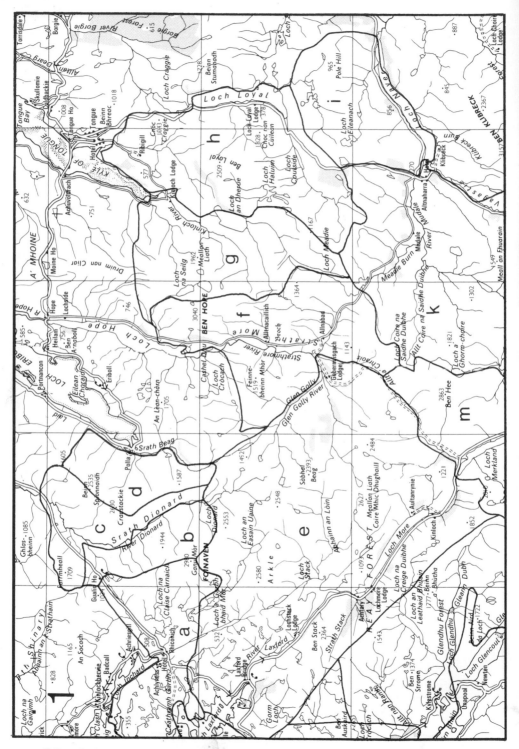

© Crown Copyright

Map 1   Reay Forest   Ben Hope

Estate Reference	Estate Name	Estate Reference	Estate Name
1/a	RHICONICH	1/g	KINLOCH
1/b	GUALIN ESTATE	1/h	BEN LOYAL
1/c	BALNAKEIL	1/i	NORTH LOCHNAVER ESTATE
1/d	RISPOND & POLLA	1/k	ALTNAHARRA ESTATE
1/e	REAY FOREST	1/m	MERKLAND
1/f	STRATHMORE		

Mountains and Mountain Groups

Beinn Spionnaidh   Cranstackie   Ben Hope

Foinaven   Arkle   Meall Horn   Ben Loyal
Meallan Liath Coire Mhic Dhughaill

                                          Ben Hee

Ben Stack

Mountain Mountain Group	Approach Routes	Estate Name	Estate Ref	Refer to page
Beinn Spionnaidh Cranstackie	From east/ Loch Eriboll	RISPOND & POLLA	1/d	90
	From west	BALNAKEIL,	1/c	90
		GUALIN ESTATE	1/b	90
Foinaven Arkle Meall Horn Meallan Liath Coire Mhic Dhughaill	Via existing paths	REAY FOREST	1/e	90
	From north	GUALIN ESTATE	1/b	90
	From north-west	RHICONICH	1/a	90
Ben Stack	From east	REAY FOREST	1/e	90

Mountain Mountain Group	Approach Routes	Estate Name	Estate Ref	Refer to page
Ben Hope	From south-west	STRATHMORE	1/f	90
	From east	KINLOCH	1/g	91
Ben Loyal	Via existing paths	BEN LOYAL	1/h	91
	From south	ALTNAHARRA ESTATE	1/k	91
	From west	KINLOCH	1/g	91
Ben Hee	From east	ALTNAHARRA ESTATE	1/k	91
	From south	MERKLAND	1/m	91
	From north-west	REAY FOREST	1/e	90

Map 2   Assynt   Coigach

Estate Reference	Estate Name	Estate Reference	Estate Name
2/a	LOCH ASSYNT ESTATE	2/g	INVERCASSLEY
2/b	KYLESTROME	2/h	DUCHALLY
2/c	REAY FOREST	2/i	INVERPOLLY
2/d	GLENCANISP AND	2/k	BENMORE
	DRUMRUNIE	2/m	BENMORE COIGACH
2/e	INCHNADAMPH	2/n	KEANCHULISH
2/f	MERKLAND	2/o	FOREST ENTERPRISE

Mountains and Mountain Groups

Quinag	Conival
Glas Bheinn	Breabag
Beinn Leoid	Cul Mor Cul Beag
Suilven Canisp	Stac Pollaidh
Ben More Assynt	Ben Mor Coigach

Mountain Mountain Group	Approach Routes	Estate Name	Estate Ref	Refer to page
Quinag	Via existing paths	LOCH ASSYNT ESTATE	2/a	91
Glas Bheinn	From west A984	INCHNADAMPH	2/e	92
Beinn Leoid	From east A839	REAY FOREST	2/c	92
		KYLESTROME	2/b	91
Suilven	From west Lochinver and Suileag or Inverkirkaig and River Kirkaig	GLENCANISP AND DRUMRUNIE	2/d	92
Canisp	From east A837	GLENCANISP AND DRUMRUNIE	2/d	92

Map on next page

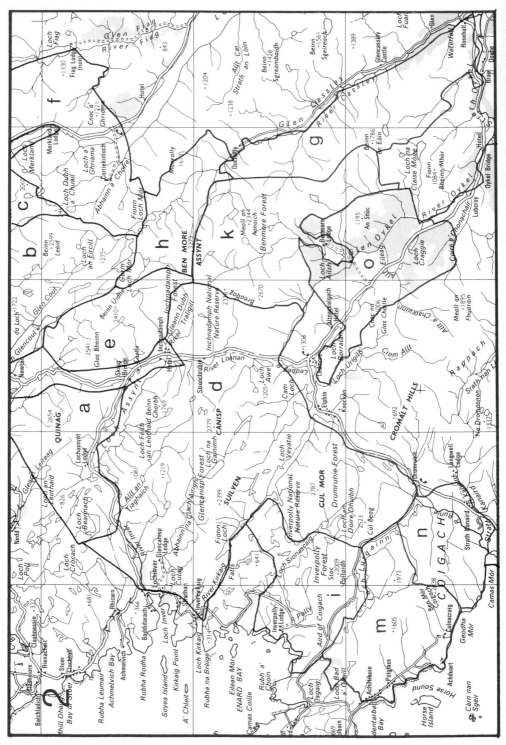

Mountain Mountain Group	Approach Routes	Estate Name	Estate Ref	Refer to page
Ben More Assynt Conival	From west Inchnadamph approach via Gleann Dubh	INCHNADAMPH GLENCANISP AND DRUMRUNIE	2/e 2/d	92 92
	From south Loch Ailsh and Glen Oykel	BENMORE FOREST ENTERPRISE	2/k 2/o	93 93
	From north	KYLESTROME	2/b	91
	From north-east	MERKLAND	2/f	92
	From east	DUCHALLY INVERCASSLEY	2/h 2/g	92 92
Breabag	From west A837	GLENCANISP AND DRUMRUNIE	2/d	92
	From Inchnadamph by Gleann Dubh	INCHNADAMPH GLENCANISP AND DRUMRUNIE	2/e 2/d	92 92
Cul Mor Cul Beag	All routes	GLENCANISP AND DRUMRUNIE	2/d	92
Stac Pollaidh	From south Loch Lurgainn	INVERPOLLY	2/i	92
Ben Mor Coigach	From north-west Achiltibuie	BENMORE COIGACH	2/m	93
	From southern limit of Loch Lurgainn on the Drumrunie to Achiltibuie road	KEANCHULISH	2/n	93

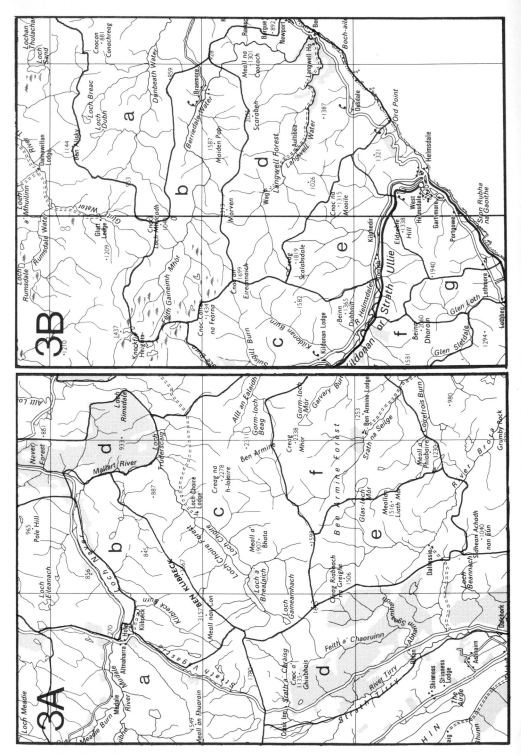

Map 3A   Klibreck

Estate Reference	Estate Name	Estate Reference	Estate Name
3A/a	ALTNAHARRA ESTATE	3A/d	FOREST ENTERPRISE
3A/b	CLEBRIG	3A/e	DALNESSIE ESTATE
3A/c	LOCH CHOIRE ESTATE	3A/f	BEN ARMINE

Mountains and Mountain Groups

Ben Klibreck   Creag Mhor

Map 3B   Morven

Estate Reference	Estate Name	Estate Reference	Estate Name
3B/a	DUNBEATH	3B/e	TORRISH
3B/b	BRAEMORE	3B/f	KILDONAN
3B/c	SUISGILL	3B/g	CRAKAIG
3B/d	LANGWELL		

Mountains and Mountain Groups

Morven   Scaraben   Beinn Dhorain

Mountain Mountain Group	Approach Routes	Estate Name	Estate Ref	Refer to page
Ben Klibreck	From west/A836 between Altnaharra and Crask Inn	ALTNAHARRA ESTATE	3A/a	93
		CLEBRIG	3A/b	93
	From west and north	CLEBRIG	3A/b	93
	From east and south	LOCH CHOIRE ESTATE	3A/c	93

Mountain Mountain Group	Approach Routes	Estate Name	Estate Ref	Refer to page
Creag Mhor	From north	LOCH CHOIRE ESTATE	3A/c	93
	From south	BEN ARMINE	3A/f	94
	From south-west	DALNESSIE ESTATE	3A/e	94
Morven Scaraben	All approaches	BRAEMORE	3B/b	94
		LANGWELL	3B/d	94
		SUISGILL	3B/c	94
Beinn Dhorain	From Strath Ullie	TORRISH	3B/e	95
		KILDONAN	3B/f	95
	From south-east	CRAKAIG	3B/g	95

Map 4   Loch Broom   Ben Wyvis

Estate Reference	Estate Name	Estate Reference	Estate Name
4/a	INVERLAEL DEER FOREST	4/i	WEST FANNICH
		4/k	FANNICH
4/b	ALLADALE & DEANICH	4/m	LOCHLUICHART
4/c	FORREST FARM	4/n	STRATHVAICH ESTATE
4/d	GLENCALVIE	4/o	KILDERMORIE
4/e	INVERLAEL	4/p	FOREST ENTERPRISE
4/f	BRAEMORE	4/q	WYVIS
4/g	INVERBROOM	4/r	FOREST ENTERPRISE
4/h	FOICH ESTATE	4/s	CORRIEMOILLIE

Mountains and Mountain Groups

Beinn Dearg Group	Carn Chuinneag
Seana Bhraigh	Western Fannaichs
Carn Ban	Eastern Fannaichs
Beinn a' Chaisteil	Ben Wyvis Little Wyvis

Mountain Mountain Group	Approach Routes	Estate Name	Estate Ref	Refer to page
Beinn Dearg Group	By Gleann na Sguaib	INVERLAEL DEER FOREST	4/a	95
	From Dirrie More	BRAEMORE	4/f	96
	From south-east	STRATHVAICH ESTATE	4/n	97
	From north-east	ALLADALE & DEANICH	4/b	95
		INVERLAEL	4/e	96
Seana Bhraigh	From Inverlael	INVERLAEL DEER FOREST	4/a	95
	From east	ALLADALE & DEANICH	4/b	95

Map on next page

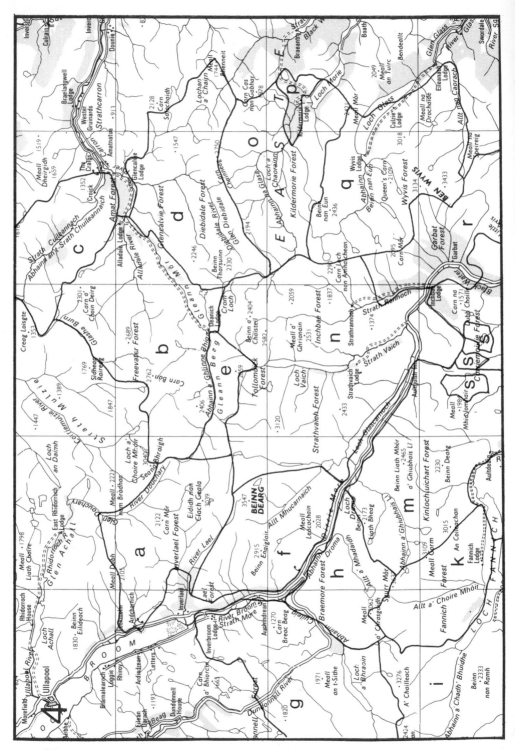

© Crown Copyright

Mountain Mountain Group	Approach Routes	Estate Name	Estate Ref	Refer to page
Carn Ban	From west	ALLADALE & DEANICH	4/b	95
	From south	STRATHVAICH ESTATE	4/n	97
		INVERLAEL	4/e	96
Beinn a' Chaisteil	From south	STRATHVAICH ESTATE	4/n	97
Carn Chuinneag	From south-east	KILDERMORIE	4/o	97
	From north	GLENCALVIE	4/d	95
Western Fannaichs	Loch a' Bhraoin & north-western approach	INVERBROOM	4/g	96
		WEST FANNICH	4/i	96
		FANNICH	4/k	96
	From south	WEST FANNICH	4/i	96
		FANNICH	4/k	96
Eastern Fannaichs	From north	FOICH ESTATE	4/h	96
	All routes	FANNICH	4/k	96
		LOCHLUICHART	4/m	96
	From Gorstan	CORRIEMOILLIE	4/s	97
		LOCHLUICHART	4/m	96
Ben Wyvis	From east	WYVIS	4/q	97
	From west and south	FOREST ENTERPRISE	4/r	97
Little Wyvis	From west	FOREST ENTERPRISE	4/r	97

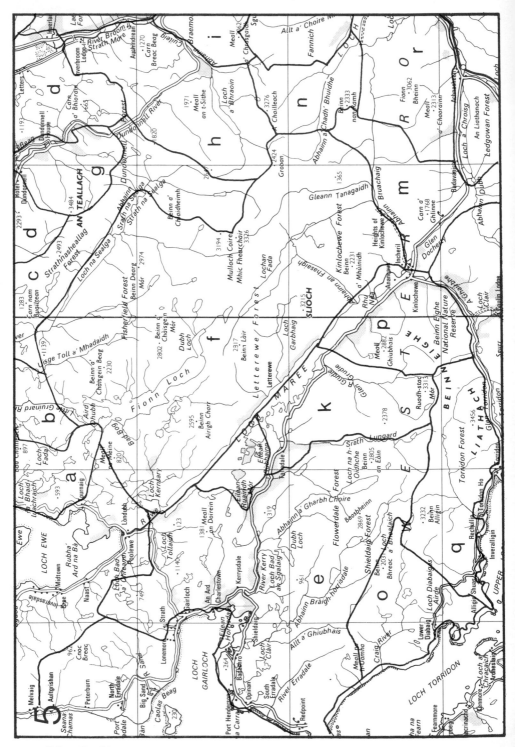

© Crown Copyright

Map 5   Dundonnell   Torridon

Estate Reference	Estate Name	Estate Reference	Estate Name
5/a	TOURNAIG	5/h	INVERBROOM
5/b	LITTLE GRUINARD	5/i	FOICH ESTATE
5/c	GRUINARD	5/k	GRUDIE & TALLADALE
5/d	DUNDONNELL	5/m	KINLOCHEWE
5/e	GAIRLOCH	5/n	WEST FANNICH
5/f	ARDLAIR	5/o	DIABAIG
	FISHERFIELD	5/p	BEINN EIGHE NATIONAL
	LETTEREWE		NATURE RESERVE
5/g	EILEAN DARACH	5/q	TORRIDON
		5/r	LOCH ROSQUE

Mountains and Mountain Groups

Beinn Airigh Charr   Beinn Lair
Beinn a' Chaisgein Mor
Beinn Dearg Bheag
Beinn Dearg Mor
Ruadh Stac Mor
A' Mhaighdean

An Teallach

Beinn a' Chlaidheimh

Creag Rainich

Sgurr Ban
Mullach Coire Mhic Fhearchair
Beinn Tarsuinn

Slioch   Beinn a' Mhuinidh

A' Chailleach   Sgurr Breac

Fionn Bheinn

Meall a' Ghiubhais
Ruadh-stac Beag

Beinn Eighe
Liathach

Beinn Alligin
Beinn Dearg
Baosbheinn
Beinn an Eoin

Mountain Mountain Group	Approach Routes	Estate Name	Estate Ref	Refer to page
Beinn Airigh Charr Beinn Lair Beinn a' Chaisgein Mor Beinn Dearg Bheag Beinn Dearg Mor Ruadh Stac Mor A' Mhaighdean	All approaches	ARDLAIR FISHERFIELD LETTEREWE	5/f	98
	From north	TOURNAIG LITTLE GRUINARD GRUINARD	5/a 5/b 5/c	97 98 98
	From east	EILEAN DARACH GRUINARD	5/g 5/c	98 98
An Teallach	From north	DUNDONNELL	5/d	98
	From north-west and west	GRUINARD	5/c	98
	From east and south-east	EILEAN DARACH	5/g	98
Beinn a' Chlaidheimh	Corrie Hallie	EILEAN DARACH GRUINARD	5/g 5/c	98 98
	Loch a' Bhraoin	INVERBROOM	5/h	98
Creag Rainich	Loch a' Bhraoin	INVERBROOM	5/h	98
Sgurr Ban Mullach Coire Mhic Fhearchair Beinn Tarsuinn	Carnmore approach	ARDLAIR FISHERFIELD LETTEREWE	5/f	98
	From north-east	EILEAN DARACH GRUINARD	5/g 5/c	98 98
	Loch a' Bhraoin	INVERBROOM	5/h	98
	Heights of Kinlochewe approach	ARDLAIR FISHERFIELD LETTEREWE	5/f	98

Mountain Mountain Group	Approach Routes	Estate Name	Estate Ref	Refer to page
Slioch Beinn a' Mhuinidh	All approaches	ARDLAIR FISHERFIELD LETTEREWE	5/f	98
	From south-east	KINLOCHEWE	5/m	99
A' Chailleach Sgurr Breac	From north	INVERBROOM FOICH ESTATE	5/h 5/i	98 98
	From south and south-west	WEST FANNICH LOCH ROSQUE KINLOCHEWE	5/n 5/r 5/m	99 99 99
Fionn Bheinn	Achnasheen	LOCH ROSQUE	5/r	99
Meall a' Ghiubhais Ruadh-stac Beag	From east	BEINN EIGHE NATIONAL NATURE RESERVE	5/p	99
Beinn Eighe Liathach	Glen Grudie	GRUDIE AND TALLADALE	5/k	99
	Anancaun Centre Kinlochewe and Loch Bharranch	BEINN EIGHE NATIONAL NATURE RESERVE	5/p	99
	From south and west	TORRIDON	5/q	99
Beinn Alligin Beinn Dearg Baosbheinn Beinn an Eoin	Northern approaches	GAIRLOCH	5/e	98
	From west	DIABAIG	5/o	99
	From south	TORRIDON	5/q	99
	From east	GRUDIE AND TALLADALE	5/k	99

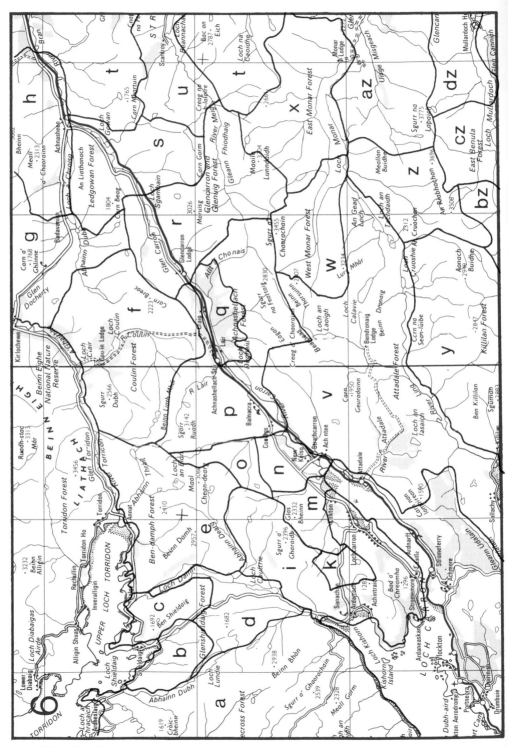

© Crown Copyright

Map 6   Glen Carron

Estate Reference	Estate Name	Estate Reference	Estate Name
6/a	APPLECROSS	6/r	GLENCARRON AND GLENUIG
6/b	KINLOCH		
6/c	BEN SHIELDAIG	6/s	LEDGOWAN
6/d	COULDORAN	6/t	STRATHCONON
6/e	BEN DAMPH ESTATE	6/u	SCARDROY
6/f	COULIN	6/v	ATTADALE
6/g	KINLOCHEWE	6/w	WEST MONAR
6/h	LOCH ROSQUE	6/x	EAST MONAR
6/i	LOCHCARRON	6/y	KILLILAN
6/k	GLENMORE	6/z	PAIT
6/m	TULLICH	6/az	BRAULEN
6/n	NEW KELSO	6/bz	WEST BENULA
6/o	FIONNARAICH	6/cz	EAST BENULA
6/p	ACHNASHELLACH	6/dz	COZAC
6/q	FOREST ENTERPRISE		

Mountains and Mountain Groups

Applecross Hills

Beinn Damh

Maol Chean-dearg   An Ruadh-stac

Beinn Liath Mhor   Sgorr Ruadh
Fuar Tholl

Sgorr nan Lochan Uaine
Sgurr Dubh

Moruisg   Sgurr nan Ceannaichean

Sgurr na Feartaig   Beinn Tharsuinn

Sgurr Choinnich
Sgurr a' Chaorachain
Maoile Lunndaidh

Bidein a' Choire Sheasgaich
Lurg Mhor

Beinn Dronaig

An Socach   An Riabhachan
Sgurr na Lapaich

Mountain Mountain Group	Approach Routes	Estate Name	Estate Ref	Refer to page
Applecross Hills	All routes	APPLECROSS	6/a	100
	From north-east and east	KINLOCH COULDORAN	6/b 6/d	100 100
Beinn Damh	Annat / A896	BEN DAMPH ESTATE	6/e	100
Maol Chean-dearg An Ruadh-stac	Annat and Loch an Eion	BEN DAMPH ESTATE	6e	100
	Coulags	NEW KELSO FIONNARAICH	6/n 6/o	101 101
	From south-west	LOCHCARRON	6/i	101
Beinn Liath Mhor Sgorr Ruadh Fuar Tholl	Achnashellach and Coire Lair	ACHNASHELLACH	6/p	101
	Glen Torridon/ Ling Hut or Loch Clair	COULIN	6/f	100
	From north-west by Abhainn Thrail	BEN DAMPH ESTATE	6/e	100
Sgorr nan Lochan Uaine Sgurr Dubh	Glen Torridon	COULIN	6/f	100
Moruisg Sgurr nan Ceannaichean	Craig/ Allt a' Chonais	FOREST ENTERPRISE ACHNASHELLACH GLENCARRON AND GLENUIG	6/q 6/p 6/r	102 101 102
	Loch Sgamhain and Alltan na Feola	GLENCARRON AND GLENUIG	6/r	102
	From north-east	LEDGOWAN	6/s	102
Sgurr na Feartaig Beinn Tharsuinn	From Lair or Craig	FOREST ENTERPRISE ACHNASHELLACH	6/q 6/p	102 101
	From south-west	ATTADALE	6/v	102

Mountain / Mountain Group	Approach Routes	Estate Name	Estate Ref	Refer to page
Sgurr Choinnich	Craig/	FOREST ENTERPRISE	6/q	102
Sgurr a' Chaorachain	Allt a' Chonais	ACHNASHELLACH	6/p	101
Maoile Lunndaidh				
	From north	GLENCARRON AND GLENUIG	6/r	102
	From south/	EAST MONAR	6/x	102
	Loch Monar	WEST MONAR	6/w	102
	From east	STRATHCONON	6/t	102
		SCARDROY	6/u	102
	From south-west	ATTADALE	6/v	102
Bidein a' Choire Sheasgaich	From west	ATTADALE	6/v	102
Lurg Mhor				
	From north-east	WEST MONAR	6/w	102
	From south	KILLILAN	6/y	103
		ATTADALE	6/v	102
Beinn Dronaig	From west	ATTADALE	6/v	102
An Socach	From north and	PAIT	6/z	103
An Riabhachan	west	KILLILAN	6/y	103
Sgurr na Lapaich				
	From north and	PAIT	6/z	103
	east	BRAULEN	6/az	103
	From south	WEST BENULA	6/bz	103
	From south and	EAST BENULA	6/cz	103
	east	COZAC	6/dz	103

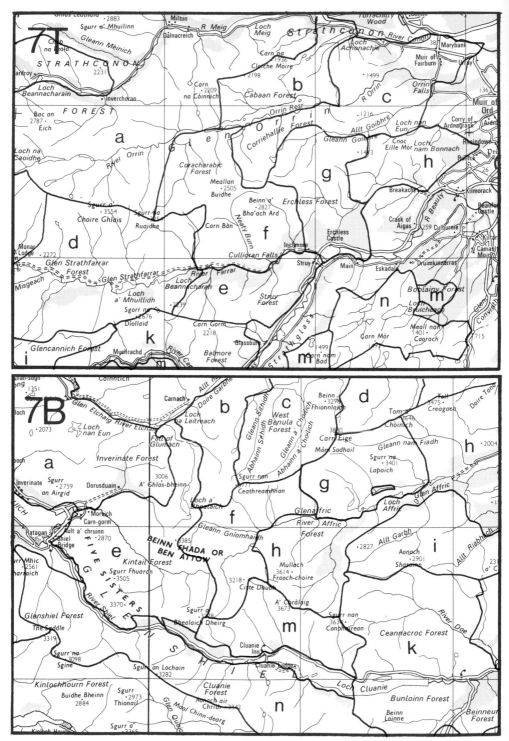

Map 7T   Strathconon   Strathfarrar

Estate Reference	Estate Name	Estate Reference	Estate Name
7T/a	STRATHCONON	7T/g	ERCHLESS
7T/b	SCATWELL ESTATE	7T/h	FARLEY ESTATE
7T/c	FAIRBURN & CORRIEHALLIE	7T/i	COZAC
		7T/k	BALMORE
7T/d	BRAULEN	7T/m	FOREST ENTERPRISE
7T/e	STRUY	7T/n	BEAUFORT & ESKADALE
7T/f	CULLIGRAN		

Mountains and Mountain Groups

Strathconon Hills

Sgurr a' Choire Ghlais Group

Meallan Buidhe
Beinn a' Bha'ach Ard

Sgorr na Diollaid   Carn Gorm

Map 7B   Kintail   Affric

Estate Reference	Estate Name	Estate Reference	Estate Name
7B/a	INVERINATE	7B/g	LOCH AFFRIC ESTATE
7B/b	GLOMACH	7B/h	FOREST ENTERPRISE
7B/c	WEST BENULA	7B/i	WESTER GUISACHAN
7B/d	EAST BENULA	7B/k	CEANNACROC ESTATE
7B/e	KINTAIL	7B/m	CORRIELAIR ESTATE
7B/f	WEST AFFRIC	7B/n	GLENSHIEL & CLUANIE

Mountains and Mountain Groups

Sgurr an Airgid

Sgurr nan Ceathreamhnan
Mullach na Dheiragain

Mam Sodhail   Carn Eighe
Beinn Fhionnlaidh

Toll Creagach   Tom a' Choinich

A' Ghlas-bheinn   Beinn Fhada

Five Sisters of Kintail   Saileag
Sgurr a' Bhealaich Dheirg Group
Ciste Dhubh Group

A' Chralaig   Mullach Fraoch-choire

Sgurr nan Conbhairean
Sail Chaorainn   Carn Ghluasaid

Carn a' Choire Ghairbh
Aonach Shasuinn

Mountain Mountain Group	Approach Routes	Estate Name	Estate Ref	Refer to page
Strathconon Hills	From Strathanmore and Inverchoran	STRATHCONON	7T/a	103
	From east	SCATWELL ESTATE FAIRBURN AND CORRIEHALLIE	7T/b 7T/c	104 104
Sgurr a' Choire Ghlais Group	From north	STRATHCONON	7T/a	103
	From Glen Strathfarrar	BRAULEN	7T/d	104
	From east	CULLIGRAN	7T/f	104
Meallan Buidhe Beinn a' Bha'ach Ard	All routes	CULLIGRAN	7T/f	104
	From north	FAIRBURN AND CORRIEHALLIE	7T/c	104
	From north-east	ERCHLESS	7T/g	105
	From south-west	BRAULEN	7T/d	104
Sgorr na Diollaid Carn Gorm	From north	BRAULEN STRUY	7T/d 7T/e	104 104
	From south	BALMORE	7T/k	105
	From south-west	COZAC	7T/i	105
Sgurr an Airgid	All approaches	INVERINATE	7B/a	105
Sgurr nan Ceathreamhnan Mullach na Dheiragain	Glen Elchaig	INVERINATE GLOMACH	7B/a 7B/b	105 105
	From north	WEST BENULA EAST BENULA	7B/c 7B/d	106 106
	Glen Affric	FOREST ENTERPRISE LOCH AFFRIC ESTATE WEST AFFRIC	7B/h 7B/g 7B/f	106 106 106
Mam Sodhail Carn Eighe Beinn Fhionnlaidh	Glen Affric	FOREST ENTERPRISE LOCH AFFRIC ESTATE	7B/h 7B/g	106 106

Mountain Mountain Group	Approach Routes	Estate Name	Estate Ref	Refer to page
Mam Sodhail Carn Eighe	Gleann a'	WEST BENULA	7B/c	106
Beinn Fhionnlaidh	Choilich	EAST BENULA	7B/d	106
Toll Creagach	Glen Affric	FOREST ENTERPRISE	7B/h	106
Tom a' Choinich		LOCH AFFRIC ESTATE	7B/g	106
A' Ghlas-bheinn	From Bealach na	INVERINATE	7B/a	105
Beinn Fhada	Sroine or Bealach an Sgairne			
	All routes	KINTAIL	7B/e	106
		WEST AFFRIC	7B/f	106
Five Sisters of Kintail	Glen Lichd	KINTAIL	7B/e	106
Saileag				
Sgurr a' Bhealaich Dheirg				
Group				
Ciste Dhubh Group				
	Glen Shiel	KINTAIL	7B/e	106
	From south-east	CORRIELAIR ESTATE	7B/m	106
	From north-east	FOREST ENTERPRISE	7B/h	106
		WEST AFFRIC	7B/f	106
A' Chralaig	Loch Cluanie	CORRIELAIR ESTATE	7B/m	106
Mullach Fraoch-choire				
	Glen Affric	FOREST ENTERPRISE	7B/h	106
Sgurr nan Conbhairean	Loch Cluanie	CORRIELAIR ESTATE	7B/m	106
Sail Chaorainn		CEANNACROC ESTATE	7B/k	106
Carn Ghluasaid				
	From north	FOREST ENTERPRISE	7B/h	106
	From north-east	WESTER GUISACHAN	7B/i	106
	From east	CEANNACROC ESTATE	7B/k	106
Carn a' Choire Ghairbh	Glen Affric	FOREST ENTERPRISE	7B/h	106
Aonach Shasuinn		WESTER GUISACHAN	7B/i	106

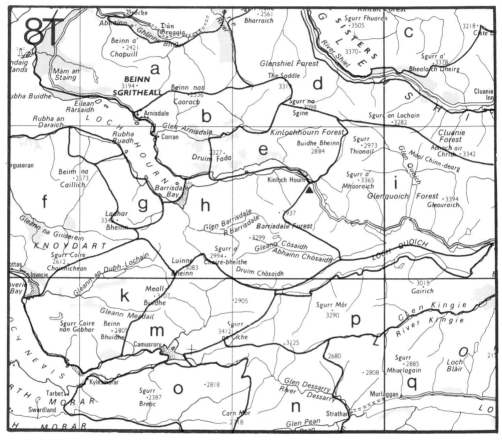

Map 8T   Knoydart

Estate Reference	Estate Name	Estate Reference	Estate Name
8T/a	EILEANREACH	8T/h	BARRISDALE
8T/b	ARNISDALE	8T/i	WESTER GLENQUOICH
8T/c	KINTAIL	8T/k	KILCHOAN
8T/d	GLENSHIEL AND CLUANIE	8T/m	CAMUSRORY
		8T/n	GLENDESSARY DEER FOREST
8T/e	KINLOCH HOURN		
8T/f	KNOYDART	8T/o	NORTH MORAR ESTATE
8T/g	LI AND COIRE DHORRCAIL	8T/p	KINGIE
		8T/q	LOCHIEL ESTATE

Mountains and Mountain Groups

Beinn Sgritheall

Beinn na h-Eaglaise
Beinn nan Caorach

The Saddle   Sgurr na Sgine
South Glen Shiel Ridge

Buidhe Bheinn

Sgurr a' Mhaoraich   Gleouraich
Spidean Mialach

Beinn na Caillich   Ladhar Bheinn
Sgurr Coire Choinnichean

Luinne Bheinn   Meall Buidhe
Beinn Bhuidhe

Sgurr a' Choire-bheithe   Ben Aden

Sgurr na Ciche
Garbh Chioch Mhor
Sgurr nan Coireachan

Sgurr Mor   Sgurr an Fhuarain

Gairich

Fraoch Bheinn   Sgurr Mhurlagain

Carn Mor

Mountain Mountain Group	Approach Routes	Estate Name	Estate Ref	Refer to page
Beinn Sgritheall	All approaches	EILEANREACH	8T/a	107
	Arnisdale	ARNISDALE	8T/b	107
Beinn na h-Eaglaise Beinn nan Caorach	Arnisdale	ARNISDALE	8T/b	107
The Saddle Sgurr na Sgine South Glen Shiel Ridge	Glen Shiel/ all approaches	GLENSHIEL AND CLUANIE	8T/d	107
	Kinloch Hourn	KINLOCH HOURN	8T/e	107
	Glen Quoich	WESTER GLENQUOICH	8T/i	108
Buidhe Bheinn	Glen Shiel	GLENSHIEL AND CLUANIE	8T/d	107
	From south	KINLOCH HOURN	8T/e	107
Sgurr a' Mhaoraich Gleouraich Spidean Mialach	All approaches	WESTER GLENQUOICH	8T/i	108
Beinn na Caillich Ladhar Bheinn Sgurr Coire Choinnichean	All routes	KNOYDART	8T/f	107
	From east	BARRISDALE	8T/h	108
	From south-east	KILCHOAN CAMUSRORY	8T/k 8T/m	108 108
Ladhar Bheinn	Coire Dhorrcail	LI AND COIRE DHORRCAIL	8T/g	107
Luinne Bheinn Meall Buidhe Beinn Bhuidhe	Loch Nevis	KILCHOAN CAMUSRORY	8T/k 8T/m	108 108
	From north	BARRISDALE	8T/h	108

Mountain Mountain Group	Approach Routes	Estate Name	Estate Ref	Refer to page
Sgurr a' Choire-bheithe Ben Aden	From north-west	BARRISDALE	8T/h	108
	Loch Nevis	CAMUSRORY	8T/m	108
	From north-east	WESTER GLENQUOICH	8T/i	108
Sgurr na Ciche Garbh Chioch Mhor Sgurr nan Coireachan	Loch Nevis	CAMUSRORY	8T/m	108
	Loch Arkaig and Glen Dessarry	LOCHIEL ESTATE GLENDESSARY DEER FOREST	8T/q 8T/n	109 108
Sgurr Mor Sgurr an Fhuarain	Loch Arkaig and Glen Dessarry	LOCHIEL ESTATE KINGIE	8T/q 8T/p	109 109
	Glen Kingie	KINGIE	8T/p	109
Gairich	Loch Quoich	KINGIE	8T/p	109
Fraoch Bheinn Sgurr Mhurlagain	Loch Arkaig	LOCHIEL ESTATE	8T/q	109
Carn Mor	Glen Pean	GLENDESSARY DEER FOREST	8T/n	108

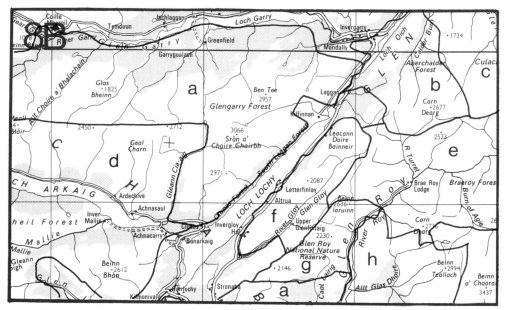

© Crown Copyright

Map 8B Loch Arkaig to Glen Garry

Estate Reference	Estate Name	Estate Reference	Estate Name
8B/a	FOREST ENTERPRISE	8B/f	GLEN GLOY ESTATE
8B/b	ABERCHALDER	8B/g	GLEN ROY NATIONAL
8B/c	CULACHY		NATURE RESERVE
8B/d	LOCHIEL ESTATE	8B/h	GLENSPEAN
8B/e	BRAEROY		

Mountains and Mountain Groups

Geal Charn   Meall na h-Eilde

Meall na Teanga
Sron a' Choire Ghairbh

Ben Tee

Beinn Iaruinn

Carn Dearg (East of Glen Roy)

Upper Glen Roy Hills

Mountain Mountain Group	Approach Routes	Estate Name	Estate Ref	Refer to page
Geall Charn Meall na h-Eilde	Loch Arkaig	LOCHIEL ESTATE	8B/d	110
	Greenfield	FOREST ENTERPRISE	8B/a	109
		LOCHIEL ESTATE	8B/d	110
Meall na Teanga Sron a' Choire Ghairbh	Loch Arkaig	FOREST ENTERPRISE	8B/a	109
	Kilfinnan and Loch Lochy	FOREST ENTERPRISE	8B/a	109
Ben Tee	Kilfinnan	FOREST ENTERPRISE	8B/a	109
	Greenfield	FOREST ENTERPRISE	8B/a	109
Beinn Iaruinn	Glen Gloy	GLEN GLOY ESTATE	8B/f	110
	Glen Roy	GLEN ROY NATIONAL NATURE RESERVE	8B/g	110
		BRAEROY	8B/e	110
Carn Dearg (east of Glen Roy)	Glen Roy	GLENSPEAN	8B/h	110
		BRAEROY	8B/e	110
Upper Glen Roy Hills	From north	ABERCHALDER	8B/b	109
	From south	BRAEROY	8B/e	110

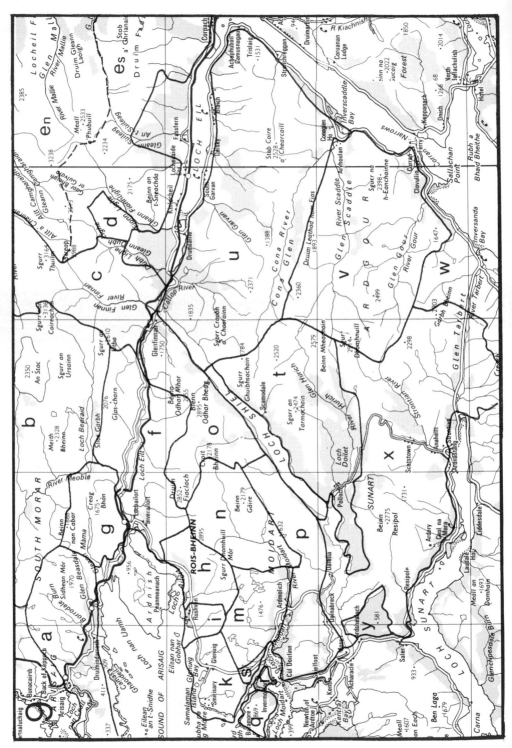

Map 9   Glenfinnan   Ardgour

Estate Reference	Estate Name	Estate Reference	Estate Name
9/a	ARISAIG	9/n	GLENMOIDART
9/b	MEOBLE AND	9/o	GLENALADALE
	LETTERMORAR	9/p	LOCHSHIEL
9/c	GLENFINNAN	9/q	EILEAN SHONA
9/d	GLEANN FIONNLIGHE	9/r	SHONA BEAG
9/e	LOCHIEL ESTATE	9/s	KYLESWOOD
9/f	INVERAILORT ESTATE	9/t	FOREST ENTERPRISE
9/g	GLEN MAMA	9/u	CONA GLEN
9/h	ROSHVEN	9/v	ARDGOUR
9/i	WEST ROSHVEN	9/w	INVERSANDA
9/k	GLENUIG	9/x	SUNART
9/m	KINLOCHMOIDART	9/y	RESIPOLE WOODLANDS

Mountains and Mountain Groups

South Morar

Sgurr nan Coireachan
Sgurr Thuilm
Streap

Braigh nan Uamhachan   Gulvain

Rois-Bheinn
Sgurr na Ba Glaise
An Stac

Beinn Odhar Bheag
Beinn Mhic Cedidh

Ardgour Group

Garbh Bheinn

Beinn Resipol

Mountain Mountain Group	Approach Routes	Estate Name	Estate Ref	Refer to page
South Morar	All routes	ARISAIG	9/a	110
		GLEN MAMA	9/g	111
Sgurr nan Coireachan Sgurr Thuilm Streap	From south	GLENFINNAN	9/c	111
	From west and south-west	MEOBLE AND LETTERMORAR	9/b	111
		INVERAILORT ESTATE	9/f	111
	From east and south-east	LOCHIEL ESTATE	9/e	111
		GLEANN FIONNLIGHE	9/d	111
Braigh nan Uamhachan Gulvain	From south and east	LOCHIEL ESTATE	9/e	111
		GLEAN FIONNLIGHE	9/d	111
Rois-Bheinn Sgurr na Ba Glaise An Stac	From north	INVERAILORT ESTATE	9/f	111
	From north-west	ROSHVEN	9/h	111
	From south and south-west	KINLOCH MOIDART	9/m	112
		GLENMOIDART	9/n	112
	From east and south-east	GLENALADALE	9/o	112
	From south	LOCHSHIEL	9/p	112
Beinn Odhar Bheag Beinn Mhic Cedidh	From north and north-west	INVERAILORT ESTATE	9/f	111
	From east and south east	GLENALADALE	9/o	112

Mountain Mountain Group	Approach Routes	Estate Name	Estate Ref	Refer to page
Ardgour Group	Callop and Cona Glen	CONA GLEN	9/u	113
	Glen Scaddle and Gleann an Lochain Duibh	ARDGOUR	9/v	113
	Glen Hurich	FOREST ENTERPRISE	9/t	113
	From south-west by Strontian River	SUNART	9/x	113
Garbh Bheinn	A861	INVERSANDA	9/w	113
Beinn Resipol	All approaches	SUNART	9/x	113

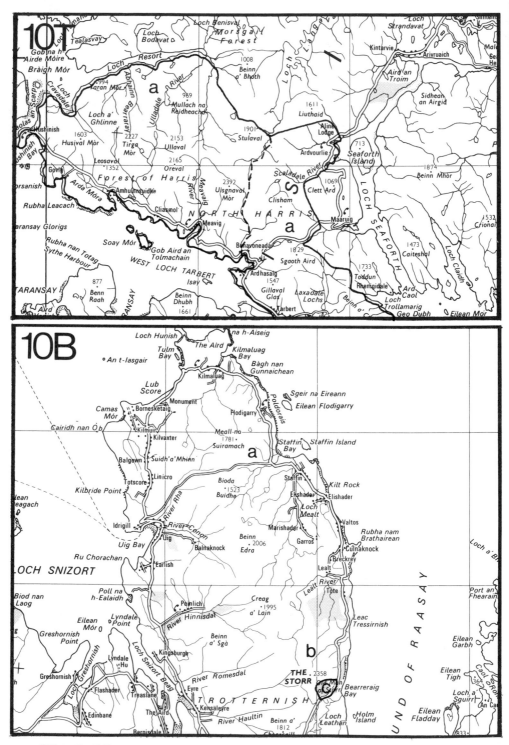

Map 10T   North Harris

Estate Reference	Estate Name		Estate Reference	Estate Name
10T/a	NORTH HARRIS ESTATE			

Mountains and Mountain Groups

Tirga Mor   Beinn Mhor
Clisham

Mountain Mountain Group	Approach Routes	Estate Name	Estate Ref	Refer to page
Tirga Mor Clisham Beinn Mhor	All approaches	NORTH HARRIS ESTATE	10T/a	114

Map 10B   Skye (Trotternish)

Estate Reference	Estate Name		Estate Reference	Estate Name
10B/a	KILMUIR		10B/c	STORR FOREST
10B/b	SCORRYBRECK			

Mountains and Mountain Groups

The Storr   Quirang

Mountain Mountain Group	Approach Routes	Estate Name	Estate Ref	Refer to page
The Storr	All approaches	SCORRYBRECK	10B/b	114
		STORR FOREST	10B/c	114
Quirang	All approaches	KILMUIR	10B/a	114

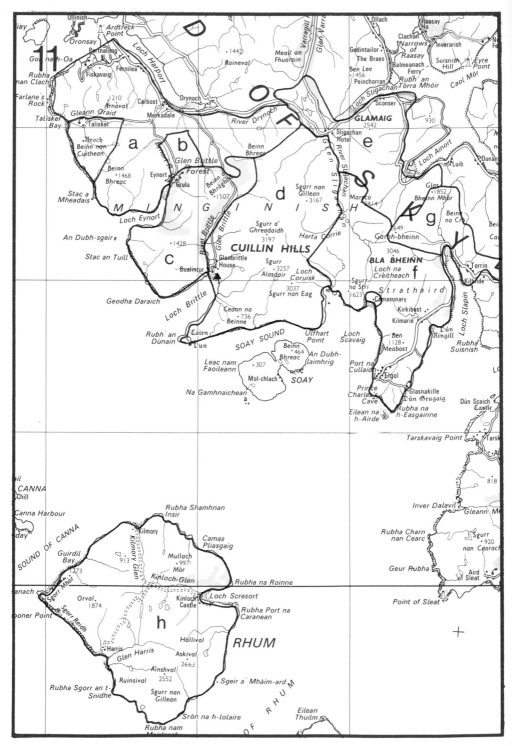

© Crown Copyright

Map 11   Skye and Rum Cuillins

Estate Reference	Estate Name	Estate Reference	Estate Name
11/a	BRACADALE	11/e	SCONSER
11/b	BRAE EYNORT CROFT	11/f	STRATHAIRD
11/c	FOREST ENTERPRISE	11/g	TORRIN
11/d	MACLEOD ESTATE	11/h	RUM

Mountains and Mountain Groups

Glamaig

Red Cuillin   Bla Bheinn

Black Cuillin

Rum Cuillin

Mountain Mountain Group	Approach Routes	Estate Name	Estate Ref	Refer to page
Glamaig	All routes	SCONSER	11/e	115
Black Cuillin	All routes	MACLEOD ESTATE	11/d	115
	From west	FOREST ENTERPRISE	11/c	114
Red Cuillin Bla Bheinn	From north	SCONSER	11/e	115
	From west	MACLEOD ESTATE	11/d	115
	Loch Slapin	TORRIN	11/g	115
		STRATHAIRD	11/f	115
Rum Cuillin	All routes	RUM	11/h	115

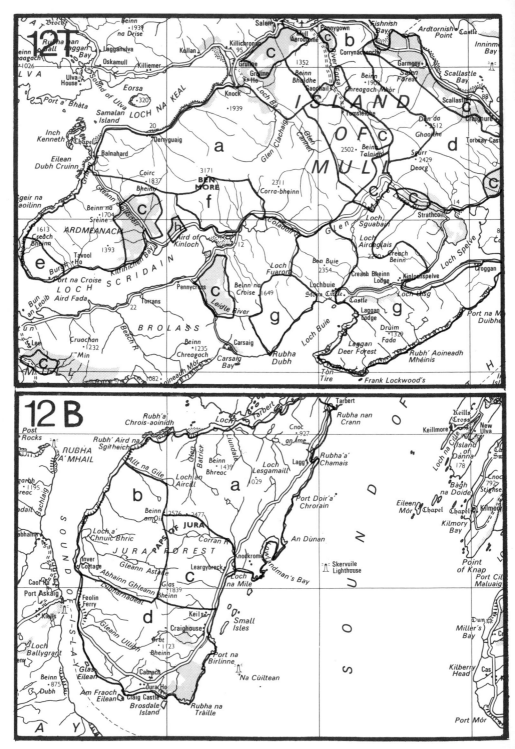

© Crown Copyright

Map 12T   Mull

Estate Reference	Estate Name	Estate Reference	Estate Name
12T/a	BENMORE ESTATE	12T/e	BURG
12T/b	GLENFORSA	12T/f	ARDVERGNISH
12T/c	FOREST ENTERPRISE	12T/g	LOCHBUIE
12T/d	TOROSAY	12/T/h	DERERACH

Mountains and Mountain Groups

Beinn Talaidh   Ben More
Dun da Ghaoithe   Corra-bheinn
Sgurr Dearg

Map 12B   South Jura

Estate Reference	Estate Name	Estate Reference	Estate Name
12B/a	TARBERT ESTATE	12B/c	FOREST ESTATE
12B/b	INVER	12B/d	ARDFIN

Mountain Group

Paps of Jura

Mountain Mountain Group	Approach Routes	Estate Name	Estate Ref	Refer to page
Beinn Talaidh Dun da Ghaoithe Sgurr Dearg	All routes	GLENFORSA	12T/b	116
	From east	TOROSAY	12T/d	116
Ben More Corra-bheinn	Loch na Keal via Dhiseig	BENMORE ESTATE	12T/a	115
	From south	ARDVERGNISH	12T/f	116
Paps of Jura	All routes	TARBERT ESTATE	12B/a	117
		INVER	12B/b	117
		FOREST ESTATE	12B/c	117
		ARDFIN	12B/d	117

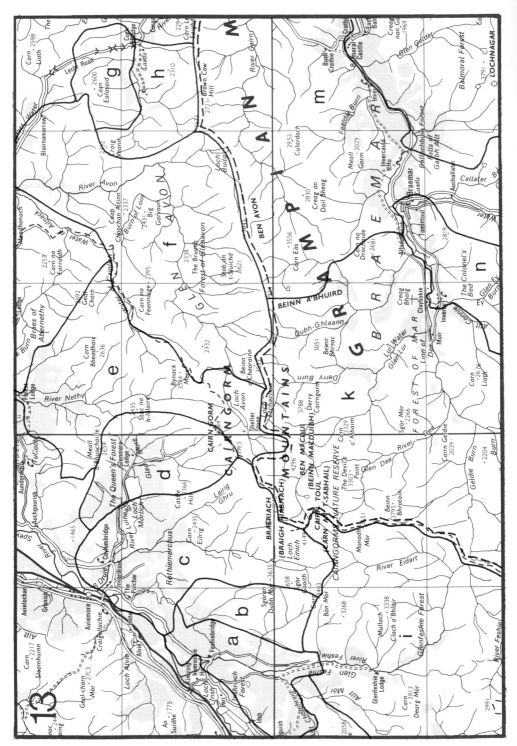

© Crown Copyright

Map 13   Cairngorms

Estate Reference	Estate Name	Estate Reference	Estate Name
13/a	FOREST ENTERPRISE	13/f	GLENAVON (INCHRORY)
13/b	INSHRIACH/	13/g	ALLARGUE
	INVERESHIE	13/h	DELNADAMPH
13/c	ROTHIEMURCHUS	13/i	GLENFESHIE
13/d	GLENMORE	13/k	MAR LODGE ESTATE
	(The Queen's Forest)	13/m	INVERCAULD
13/e	ABERNETHY FOREST	13/n	MAR ESTATE
	RESERVE		

Mar Lodge Estate, Invercauld and Mar Estate are members of the East Grampian
Deer Management Group. The Group area is defined by a broken red line; the entire
area is designated d in Section 15 on Page 60.

Mountains and Mountain Groups

Braeriach   Lairig Ghru

Cairn Gorm   Bynack More

Beinn Bhrotain
Cairn Toul
Derry Cairngorm   Ben Macdui

Beinn a' Chaorainn   Beinn Bhreac

Ben Avon   Beinn a' Bhuird

Sgor Gaoith
Mullach Clach a' Bhlair
Glen Feshie Hills

Mountain Mountain Group	Approach Routes	Estate Name	Estate Ref	Refer to page
Braeriach Lairig Ghru	Glen Einich and Coylumbridge	ROTHIEMURCHUS	13/c	117
	From north-east	GLENMORE	13/d	117
	From south	MAR LODGE ESTATE	13/k	118
Cairn Gorm Bynack More	Strath Nethy	ABERNETHY FOREST RESERVE	13/e	117
	From east	GLENAVON (INCHRORY)	13/f	118
	From south	MAR LODGE ESTATE	13/k	118

Mountain Mountain Group	Approach Routes	Estate Name	Estate Ref	Refer to page
Beinn Bhrotain Cairn Toul Ben Macdui Derry Cairngorm	From north	ROTHIEMURCHUS	13/c	117
	From north and east	GLENAVON (INCHRORY)	13/f	118
	From south and east	MAR LODGE ESTATE	13/k	118
Beinn a' Chaorainn Beinn Bhreac	From north-east	GLENAVON (INCHRORY)	13/f	118
	From south and west	MAR LODGE ESTATE	13/k	118
Ben Avon Beinn a' Bhuird	Glen Avon	GLENAVON (INCHRORY)	13/f	118
	From north-east	ALLARGUE DELNADAMPH	13/g 13/h	118 118
	Gleann an t-Slugain and Glen Gairn	INVERCAULD	13/m	118
	From south-west	MAR LODGE ESTATE	13/k	118
Sgor Gaoith Glen Feshie Hills	Feshiebridge	FOREST ENTERPRISE INSHRIACH/ INVERESHIE	13/a 13/b	117 117
Mullach Clach a' Bhlair Glen Feshie Hills	Glen Feshie	GLENFESHIE	13/i	118

Map 14   Drumochter   Glen Tilt

Estate Reference	Estate Name	Estate Reference	Estate Name
14/a	PHONES ETTERIDGE & CUAICH	14/i	CORRIEVARKIE
		14/k	TALLADH-A-BHEITH
14/b	GAICK	14/m	CRAIGANOUR
14/c	GLENFESHIE	14/n	DALNASPIDAL
14/d	MAR LODGE ESTATE	14/o	DUNALASTAIR
14/e	NORTH AND SOUTH DRUMOCHTER	14/p	FOREST ENTERPRISE
		14/q	LUDE
14/f	DALNACARDOCH	14/r	GLENFERNATE
14/g	ATHOLL	14/s	URRARD
14/h	FEALAR	14/t	BALEDMUND

Mountains and Mountain Groups

Carn na Caim
A' Bhuidheanach Beag

An Sgarsoch   Carn an Fhidhleir
Beinn Bhreac

Beinn Dearg   Carn a' Chlamain
Beinn Mheadhonach

Beinn a' Ghlo

Ben Vrackie

Beinn a' Chuallaich

Beinn Mholach
Stob an Aonaich Mhoir

Sow of Atholl   Sgairneach Mhor
Beinn Udlamain   Geal Charn

Mountain Mountain Group	Approach Routes	Estate Name	Estate Ref	Refer to page
Carn na Caim A' Bhuidheanach Beag	From north	PHONES ETTERIDGE & CUAICH	14/a	119
	From west	NORTH AND SOUTH DRUMOCHTER	14/e	119
	From south	DALNACARDOCH	14/f	119

Map on next page

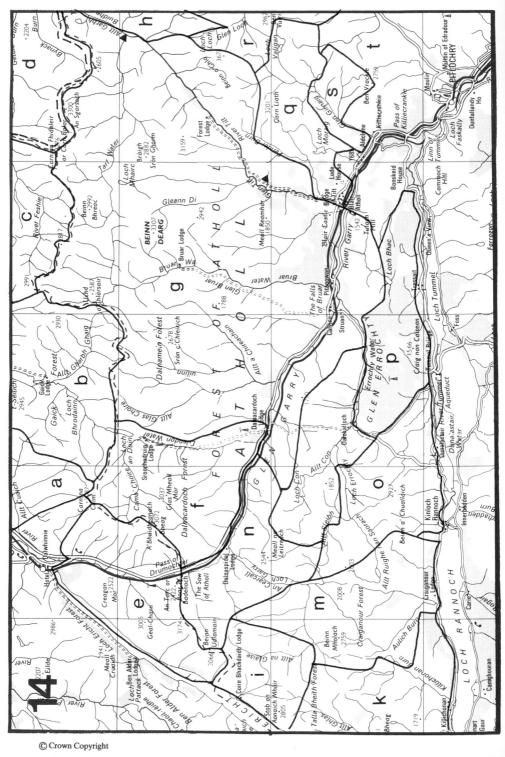

© Crown Copyright

Mountain Mountain Group	Approach Routes	Estate Name	Estate Ref	Refer to page
An Sgarsoch Carn an Fhidhleir Beinn Bhreac	Glen Feshie	GLENFESHIE	14/c	119
	From north-east/ Linn of Dee	MAR LODGE ESTATE	14/d	119
	From south	ATHOLL	14/g	120
Beinn Dearg Carn a' Chlamain Beinn Mheadhonach	All approaches	ATHOLL	14/g	120
Beinn a' Ghlo	Old Blair and Glen Tilt	ATHOLL	14/g	120
	Glen Fender/ Loch Moraig	LUDE	14/q	121
	From east or from north by path from Glen Tilt	FEALAR	14/h	120
	Glen Loch	GLENFERNATE	14/r	121
Ben Vrackie	Glen Girnaig	URRARD	14/s	121
	A9	BALEDMUND	14/t	121
Beinn a' Chuallaich	From east	DUNALASTAIR	14/o	121
Beinn Mholach Stob an Aonaich Mhoir	A9 and Loch Garry	DALNASPIDAL CRAIGANOUR CORRIEVARKIE	14/n 14/m 14/i	121 120 120
Sow of Atholl Sgairneach Mhor Beinn Udlamain Geal Charn	A9	DALNASPIDAL NORTH AND SOUTH DRUMOCHTER	14/n 14/e	121 119

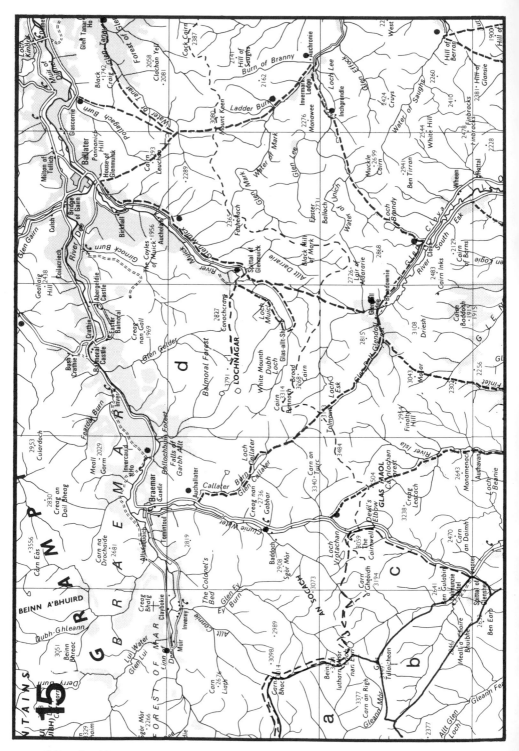

© Crown Copyright

Map 15 Glenshee Lochnagar

Estate Reference	Estate Name	Estate Reference	Estate Name
15/a	FEALAR	15/c	INVERCAULD (Land outwith
15/b	DALMUNZIE		EGDMG Area)
15/d	EAST GRAMPIAN DEER MANAGEMENT GROUP AREA		

Estates within the Group

d/1	INVERCAULD	d/8	HUNTHILL
d/2	MAR ESTATE	d/9	MILLDEN
d/3	MAR LODGE ESTATE	d/10	GLENDYE
d/4	BALMORAL	d/11	DINNET
d/5	GLENMUICK	d/12	AIRLIE
d/6	GLEN TANAR ESTATE	d/13	GLENPROSEN
d/7	INVERMARK	d/14	TULCHAN

The boundary of the East Grampian Deer Management Group Area is marked on the map with a broken red line and designated d. The recognised hill tracks within the area are shown as broken black lines. Locations of access notices are marked with a red dot. The map of the entire EGDMG area on page 62 shows estate references and estate boundaries.

Mountains and Mountain Groups

Carn Bhac An Socach	Carn an t-Sagairt Mor Tolmount	
Carn an Righ		
Glas Tulaichean The Cairnwell	Cairn of Claise Glas Maol	
	Creag Leacach	
Lochnagar Broad Cairn		
Cairn Bannoch	Monamenach	
Mount Keen	Driesh Mayar Ben Tirran	

Mountain Mountain Group	Approach Routes	Estate Name	Estate Ref	Refer to page
Carn Bhac An Socach	Glen Ey	MAR ESTATE	15/d/2	122
Carn an Righ		INVERCAULD	15/c	122
Glas Tulaichean		FEALAR	15/a	122
The Cairnwell				
	Glen Clunie and	INVERCAULD	15/d/1	122
	Devil's Elbow	FEALAR	15/a	122

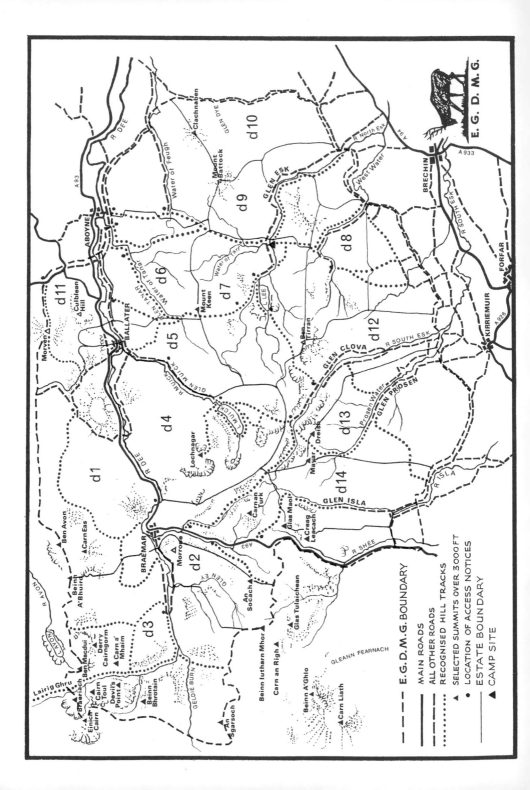

E. G. D. M. G.

--- E.G.D.M.G. BOUNDARY

——— MAIN ROADS

-- -- ALL OTHER ROADS

••••••• RECOGNISED HILL TRACKS

▲ SELECTED SUMMITS OVER 3000 FT

• LOCATION OF ACCESS NOTICES

——— ESTATE BOUNDARY

▲ CAMP SITE

Mountain Mountain Group	Approach Routes	Estate Name	Estate Ref	Refer to page
Carn Bhac An Socach	Spittal of	INVERCAULD	15/c	122
Carn an Righ	Glenshee	DALMUNZIE	15/b	122
Glas Tulaichean		FEALAR	15/a	122
Lochnagar Broad Cairn Cairn Bannoch	All routes	BALMORAL	15/d/4	123
	From west Glen Callater	INVERCAULD	15/d/1	122
	From Glen Clova and Glen Doll	AIRLIE BALMORAL	15/d/12 15/d/4	124 123
Mount Keen	Glen Tanar	GLEN TANAR ESTATE	15/d/6	123
	Glen Muick	GLENMUICK	15/d/5	123
	Glen Esk	INVERMARK	15/d/7	123
Carn an t-Sagairt Mor Tolmount	Glen Callater	INVERCAULD	15/d/1	122
	Glen Doll	AIRLIE	15/d/12	124
Cairn of Claise Glas Maol Creag Leacach	A93	INVERCAULD	15/d/1	122
	Glen Isla Caenlochan	TULCHAN	15/d/14	124
Monamenach	A93	INVERCAULD	15/d/1	122
	Glen Isla	TULCHAN	15/d/14	124
Driesh Mayar	Glen Prosen	GLENPROSEN	15/d/13	124
	Glen Doll	AIRLIE	15/d/12	124
	Glen Isla	TULCHAN	15/d/14	124
Ben Tirran	Glen Clova	AIRLIE	15/d/12	124
	From east	INVERMARK HUNTHILL	15/d/7 15/d/8	123 123

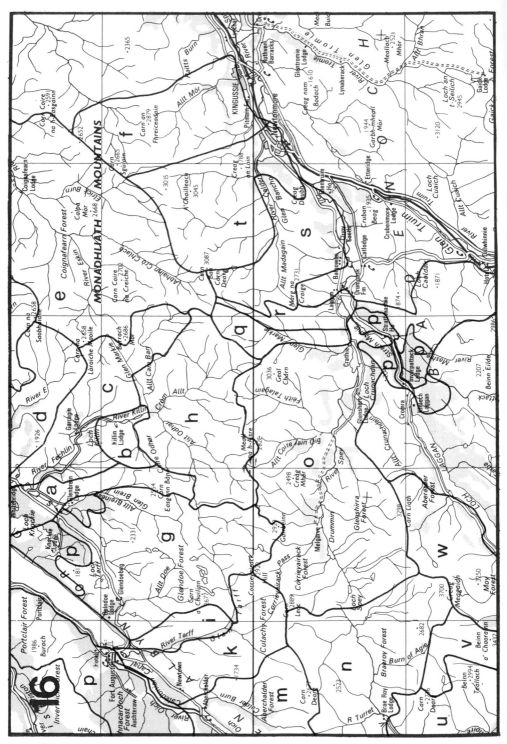

Map 16   Monadhliath   Creag Meagaidh

Estate Reference	Estate Name	Estate Reference	Estate Name
16/a	DELL	16/o	GLENSHIRRA AND SHERAMORE
16/b	KILLIN	16/p	FOREST ENTERPRISE
16/c	GARROGIE	16/q	DALCHULLY
16/d	CORRIEGARTH	16/r	BLARAGIE
16/e	COIGNAFEARN	16/s	CLUNY
16/f	PITMAIN	16/t	GLENBANCHOR
16/g	GLENDOE	16/u	GLENSPEAN
16/h	STRONELAIRG	16/v	TULLOCH
16/i	ARDACHY	16/w	CREAG MEAGAIDH NATIONAL NATURE RESERVE
16/k	CULACHY		
16/m	ABERCHALDER		
16/n	BRAEROY		

Mountains and Mountain Groups

Monadhliath Mountains

Meall na h-Aisre   Gairbeinn
Corrieyairack Hill

Carn Easgann Bana
Carn a' Chuilinn

Carn Liath

Creag Meagaidh

Beinn a' Chaorainn
Beinn Teallach

Mountain Mountain Group	Approach Routes	Estate Name	Estate Ref	Refer to page
Monadhliath Mountains	From north-west	DELL	16/a	124
		KILLIN	16/b	124
		GARROGIE	16/c	124
		CORRIEGARTH	16/d	125
	From north-east	COIGNAFEARN	16/e	125
	Kingussie	PITMAIN	16/f	125
	Glen Banchor	GLENBANCHOR	16/t	127
	Strath an Eilich	CLUNY	16/s	127

Mountain Mountain Group	Approach Routes	Estate Name	Estate Ref	Refer to page
Monadhliath Mountains	Glen Markie	GLENSHIRRA AND SHERAMORE	16/o	126
		DALCHULLY	16/q	126
		BLARAGIE	16/r	127
	From west	STRONELAIRG	16/h	125
Meall na h-Aisre Gairbeinn Corrieyairack Hill	Garva Bridge	GLENSHIRRA AND SHERAMORE	16/o	126
Carn Easgann Bana Carn a' Chuilinn	Glendoebeg	GLENDOE	16/g	125
	Glen Brein	DELL	16/a	124
Carn Liath	From north	GLENSHIRRA AND SHERAMORE	16/o	126
	Aberarder	CREAG MEAGAIDH NATIONAL NATURE RESERVE	16/w	127
Creag Meagaidh	Coire Ardair Moy Coire	CREAG MEAGAIDH NATIONAL NATURE RESERVE	16/w	127
	From north	GLENSHIRRA AND SHERRAMORE	16/o	126
	From north-west	BRAEROY	16/n	126
	From south-west	TULLOCH	16/v	127
Beinn a' Chaorainn Beinn Teallach	A86/ Roughburn	TULLOCH	16/v	127
		GLENSPEAN	16/u	127

Map 17   Ben Nevis   Ben Alder

Estate Reference	Estate Name	Estate Reference	Estate Name
17/a	FOREST ENTERPRISE	17/g	DUNAN
17/b	KILLIECHONATE	17/h	CAMUSERICHT
	WOODLANDS	17/i	BLACK CORRIES
17/c	ARDVERIKIE	17/k	RANNOCH DEER
17/d	BEN ALDER ESTATE		MANAGEMENT
17/e	KILLIECHONATE		ASSOCIATION
	AND MAMORE	17/m	GLENCOE AND DALNESS
17/f	CORROUR		

Mountains and Mountain Groups

Beinn a' Chlachair   Creag Pitridh
Geal Charn   Binnein Shuas

Stob Coire Easain
Stob a' Choire Mheadhoin
Grey Corries   Aonach Mor
Aonach Beag   Ben Nevis
The Mamores

Beinn na Lap   Chno Dearg
Stob Coire Sgriodain

Carn Dearg   Sgor Gaibhre
Ben Pharlagain

Ben Alder   Aonach Beag Group

Leum Uilleim

Stob na Cruaiche

Beinn a' Chrulaiste

Aonach Eagach

Mountain Mountain Group	Approach Routes	Estate Name	Estate Ref	Refer to page
Beinn a' Chlachair Creag Pitridh Geal Charn Binnein Shuas	Loch Laggan and River Pattack or Luiblea	ARDVERIKIE	17/c	128
	From south	BEN ALDER ESTATE	17/d	128

Map on next page

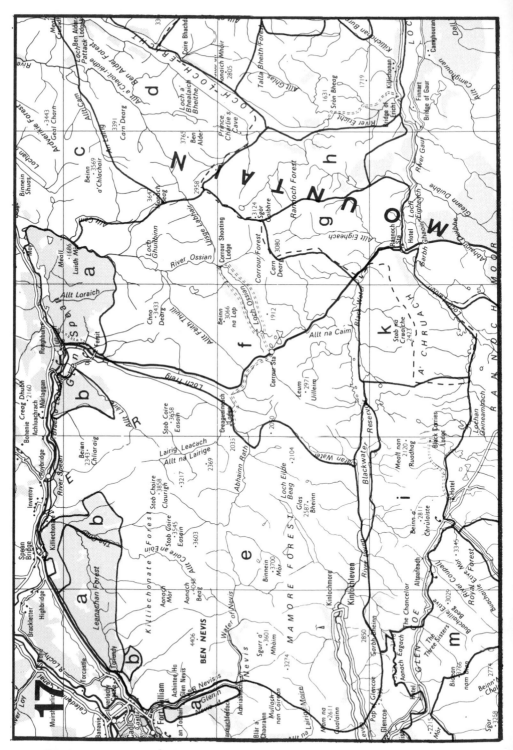

Mountain Mountain Group	Approach Routes	Estate Name	Estate Ref	Refer to page
Stob Coire Easain Stob a' Choire Mheadhoin Grey Corries Aonach Mor Aonach Beag Ben Nevis The Mamores	All routes	KILLIECHONATE AND MAMORE	17/e	128
	Spean Bridge Torlundy	FOREST ENTERPRISE	17/a	128
Beinn na Lap Chno Dearg Stob Coire Sgriodain	All routes	CORROUR	17/f	128
Carn Dearg Sgor Gaibhre Ben Pharlagain	B846 Loch Eigheach	DUNAN CAMUSERICHT	17/g 17/h	129 129
Ben Alder Aonach Beag Group	From north	ARDVERIKIE BEN ALDER ESTATE	17/c 17/d	128 128
	Loch Ossian	CORROUR BEN ALDER ESTATE	17/f 17/d	128 128
	Loch Rannoch and Ben Alder cottage	CAMUSERICHT BEN ALDER ESTATE	17/h 17/d	129 128
Leum Uilleim	Corrour Station	CORROUR	17/f	128
Stob na Cruaiche	From east	RANNOCH DEER MANAGEMENT ASSOCIATION	17/k	129
Beinn a' Chrulaiste	All approaches	BLACK CORRIES	17/i	129
Aonach Eagach	All routes	GLENCOE & DALNESS	17/m	129

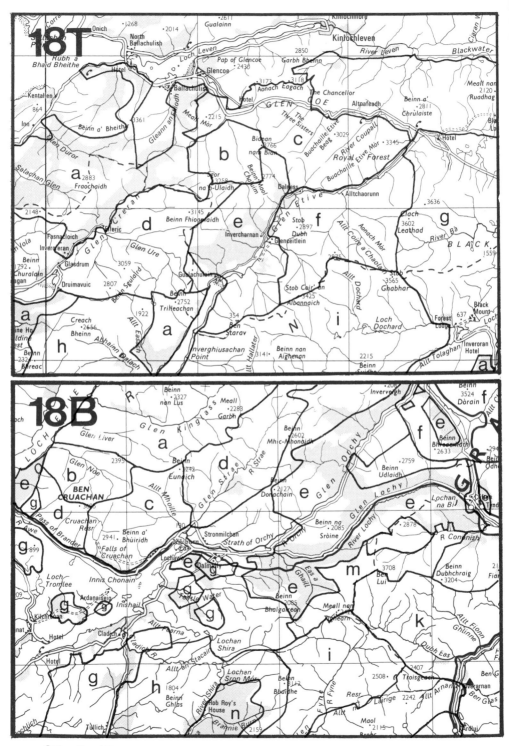

© Crown Copyright

Map 18T   Glencoe   Blackmount

Estate Reference	Estate Name	Estate Reference	Estate Name
18T/a	FOREST ENTERPRISE	18T/f	DALNESS ESTATE
18T/b	GLENLEACNAMUIDHE	18T/g	BLACKMOUNT
18T/c	GLENCOE & DALNESS	18T/h	ARDCHATTAN
18T/d	GLENCRERAN	18T/i	GLENKINGLASS
18T/e	GLEN ETIVE		

Mountains and Mountain Groups

Beinn a' Bheithir

Bidean nam Bian Group

Buachaille Etive Beag
Buachaille Etive Mor

Sgor na h-Ulaidh   Meall Lighiche

Fraochaidh

Meall a' Bhuiridh   Creise
Clach Leathad

Stob Ghabhar

Stob Coir'an Albannaich
Meall nan Eun

Ben Starav   Glas Bheinn Mhor

Beinn Fhionnlaidh

Beinn Trilleachan

Beinn Sgulaird

Creach Bheinn

Map 18B   Ben Cruachan   Ben Lui

Estate Reference	Estate Name	Estate Reference	Estate Name
18B/a	GLENKINGLASS	18B/g	TILHILL ECONOMIC FORESTRY
18B/b	GLENOE	18B/h	ARGYLL
18B/c	CASTLES ESTATE	18B/i	ARDKINGLAS
18B/d	GLENSTRAE	18B/k	GLENFALLOCH
18B/e	FOREST ENTERPRISE	18B/m	BEN LUI NATIONAL
18B/f	AUCH		NATURE RESERVE
		18B/n	FOREST ENTERPRISE

Mountains and Mountain Groups

Ben Cruachan

Beinn a' Chochuill   Beinn Eunaich

Beinn Mhic-Mhonaidh

Beinn Donachain

Beinn Udlaidh   Beinn Bhreac-liath

Ben Lui Group

Meall an Fhudair

Beinn Bhuidhe

Mountain Mountain Group	Approach Routes	Estate Name	Estate Ref	Refer to page
Beinn a' Bheithir	All routes	FOREST ENTERPRISE	18T/a	129
Bidean nam Bian Group	Glen Coe	GLENCOE & DALNESS	18T/c	130
	Glen Etive	GLEN ETIVE	18T/e	130
Buachaille Etive Beag Buachaille Etive Mor	All routes	GLENCOE & DALNESS	18T/c	130
Sgor na h-Ulaidh Meall Lighiche	Glen Creran	FOREST ENTERPRISE GLENCRERAN	18T/a 18T/d	129 130
	Gleann-leac- na-muidhe	GLENLEACNAMUIDHE	18T/b	129
	Glen Etive	GLEN ETIVE	18T/e	130
Fraochaidh	All routes	FOREST ENTERPRISE	18T/a	129
Meall a' Bhuiridh Creise Clach Leathad	From A82 and from Victoria Bridge	BLACKMOUNT	18T/g	130
	Glen Etive	DALNESS ESTATE	18T/f	130
Stob Ghabhar	Victoria Bridge	BLACKMOUNT	18T/g	130
	From south	GLENKINGLASS	18T/i	131
Stob Coir'an Albannaich Meall nan Eun	Glen Etive	GLEN ETIVE DALNESS ESTATE	18T/e 18T/f	130 130
	From south	GLENKINGLASS	18T/i	131
Ben Starav Glas Bheinn Mhor	Glen Etive	GLEN ETIVE	18T/e	130
	From south	GLENKINGLASS	18T/i	131
Beinn Fhionnlaidh	Glen Etive	GLEN ETIVE GLENCRERAN	18T/e 18T/d	130 130
Beinn Trilleachan	Glen Etive	FOREST ENTERPRISE	18T/a	129

Mountain Mountain Group	Approach Routes	Estate Name	Estate Ref	Refer to page
Beinn Sgulaird	All routes	GLENCRERAN	18T/d	130
Creach Bheinn	All routes	ARDCHATTAN	18T/h	130
Ben Cruachan	From north	GLENOE	18B/b	131
	Loch Aweside	CASTLES ESTATE	18B/c	131
		GLENSTRAE	18B/d	131
Beinn a' Chochuill Beinn Eunaich	From north	GLENKINGLASS	18B/a	131
	From south	CASTLES ESTATE	18B/c	131
	From east	GLENSTRAE	18B/d	131
Beinn Mhic-Mhonaidh Beinn Donachain	Glen Strae	GLENSTRAE	18B/d	131
	Glen Orchy	FOREST ENTERPRISE	18B/e	131
		AUCH	18B/f	131
	A82/ Coire Chailein	AUCH	18B/f	131
		FOREST ENTERPRISE	18B/e	131
Ben Lui Group	Glen Lochy	FOREST ENTERPRISE	18B/e	131
	Cononish	BEN LUI NATIONAL NATURE RESERVE	18B/m	132
	Glen Falloch	GLENFALLOCH	18B/k	132
Meall an Fhudair	Glen Falloch	GLENFALLOCH	18B/k	132
		ARDKINGLAS	18B/i	132
Beinn Bhuidhe	Glen Fyne	ARDKINGLAS	18B/i	132
	From south-west Glen Shira	ARGYLL	18B/h	132

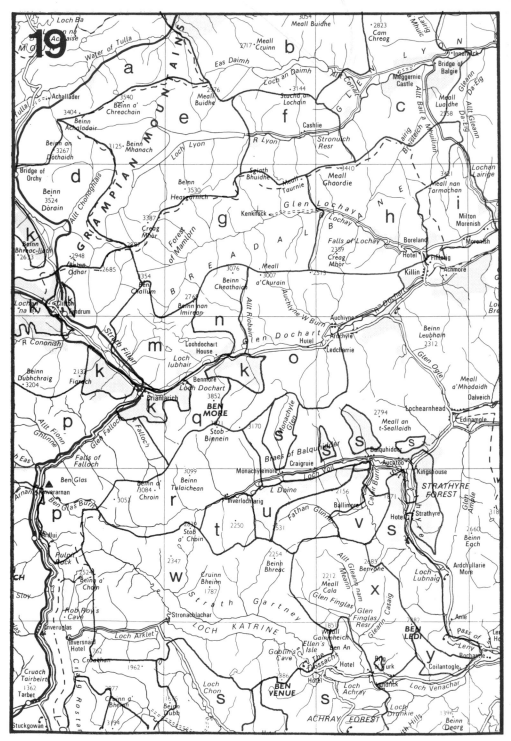

Map 19   Bridge of Orchy   Crianlarich
Trossachs

Estate Reference	Estate Name	Estate Reference	Estate Name
19/a	BLACKMOUNT	19/o	AUCHLYNE AND SUIE
19/b	LOCHS	19/p	GLENFALLOCH
19/c	MEGGERNIE	19/q	BENMORE FARM
19/d	AUCH	19/r	INVERLOCHLARIG
19/e	INVERMEARAN	19/s	FOREST ENTERPRISE
19/f	CASHLIE	19/t	BLAIRCREICH
19/g	GLEN LOCHAY	19/u	MONACHYLE TUARACH
19/h	BORELAND	19/v	IMMEREON
19/i	MORENISH	19/w	LOCH KATRINE
19/k	FOREST ENTERPRISE	19/x	GLENFINGLAS
19/m	LOCHDOCHART	19/y	MILTON OF CALLANDER
19/n	AUCHESSAN		

Mountains and Mountain Groups

Meall Buidhe   Stuchd an Lochain

Sron a' Choire Chnapanich
Meall Buidhe

Beinn a' Chreachain
Beinn Achaladair
Beinn an Dothaidh
Beinn Mhanach

Beinn Dorain

Ben Challum   Creag Mhor
Beinn Heasgarnich

Meall Ghaordie

Meall nan Tarmachan
Beinn nan Oighreag

Sgiath Chuil   Meall Glas
Beinn nan Imirean

Ben More   Stob Binnien

Cruach Ardrain   An Caisteal
Beinn a' Chroin   Beinn Tulaichean

Beinn Chabhair

Ben Venue   Ben A'an

Ben Ledi   Benvane

Mountain Mountain Group	Approach Routes	Estate Name	Estate Ref	Refer to page
Meall Buidhe Stuchd an Lochain	Loch an Daimh	LOCHS	19/b	133
	Cashlie	CASHLIE LOCHS	19/f 19/b	133 133
	From east	MEGGERNIE	19/c	133
Sron a' Choire Chnapanich Meall Buidhe	Loch Lyon	INVERMEARAN CASHLIE	19/e 19/f	133 133
Beinn a' Chreachain Beinn Achaladair Beinn an Dothaidh Beinn Mhanach	Achallader	BLACKMOUNT INVERMEARAN	19/a 19/e	132 133
	Auch Gleann	AUCH INVERMEARAN	19/d 19/e	133 133
Beinn Dorain	All approaches	AUCH	19/d	133
Ben Challum Creag Mhor	Glen Lochay	GLEN LOCHAY	19/g	133
Beinn Heasgarnich	From west	AUCH	19/d	133
	From south	LOCHDOCHART	19/m	134
Meall Ghaordie	Glen Lochay	BORELAND	19/h	134
	Glen Lyon	CASHLIE MEGGERNIE	19/f 19/c	133 133
Meall nan Tarmachan Beinn nan Oighreag	From north	MEGGERNIE BORELAND	19/c 19/h	133 134
	Glen Lochay	BORELAND	19/h	134
	Loch na Lairige east and south	MORENISH	19/i	134

Mountain Mountain Group	Approach Routes	Estate Name	Estate Ref	Refer to page
Sgiath Chuil Meall Glas	Glen Lochay	GLEN LOCHAY	19/g	133
Beinn nan Imirean	Glen Dochart	AUCHESSAN	19/n	134
	From south-west	LOCHDOCHART	19/m	134
Ben More Stob Binnein	Glen Dochart	AUCHLYNE & SUIE FOREST ENTERPRISE	19/o 19/k	135 134
	Crianlarich	BENMORE FARM FOREST ENTERPRISE	19/q 19/k	134 134
	Inverlochlarig	INVERLOCHLARIG	19/r	135
Cruach Ardrain An Caisteal Beinn a' Chroin Beinn Tulaichean	Glen Falloch	GLENFALLOCH	19/p	135
	Crianlarich	FOREST ENTERPRISE BENMORE FARM	19/k 19/q	134 134
	Inverlochlarig	INVERLOCHLARIG	19/r	135
Beinn Chabhair	From west	GLENFALLOCH	19/p	135
	From east	INVERLOCHLARIG	19/r	135
Ben Venue Ben A'an	All routes	LOCH KATRINE FOREST ENTERPRISE	19/w 19/s	136 135
Ben Ledi Benvane	Glen Finglas	GLENFINGLAS	19/x	136
	Coilantogle Farm Loch Venachar	MILTON OF CALLANDER	19/y	136
	Loch Lubnaig	FOREST ENTERPRISE	19/s	135
	Loch Voil	IMMEREON	19/v	136

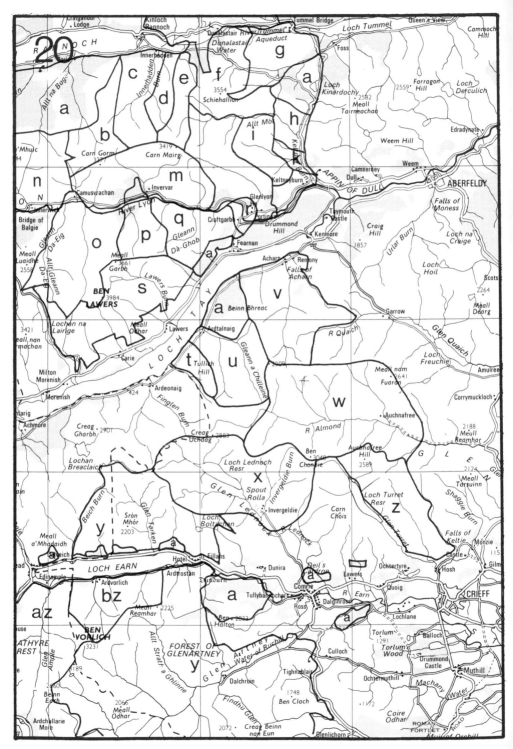

© Crown Copyright

Map 20   Loch Tay   Loch Earn

Estate Reference	Estate Name	Estate Reference	Estate Name
20/a	FOREST ENTERPRISE	20/p	INVERINAIN
20/b	CORRIE CARIE	20/q	SOUTH CHESTHILL
20/c	INNERHADDEN	20/r	CULDAREMORE
20/d	DALCHOSNIE	20/s	BEN LAWERS
20/e	WEST TEMPAR	20/t	WESTER TULLICH
20/f	CROSSMOUNT	20/u	ARDTALNAIG
20/g	KYNACHAN	20/v	REMONY
20/h	GLENGOULANDIE	20/w	AUCHNAFREE
20/i	GARTH	20/x	INVERGELDIE
20/k	INCHGARTH	20/y	DRUMMOND ESTATES
20/m	NORTH CHESTHILL	20/z	GLEN TURRET
20/n	INNERWICK	20/az	GLENAMPLE ESTATE
20/o	RORO	20/bz	ARDVORLICH

Mountains and Mountain Groups

Schichallion

Carn Gorm   Meall Garbh
Creag Mhor   Carn Mairg

Ben Lawers Group

Meall nam Fuaran

Creagan na Beinne

Creag Uchdag

Ben Chonzie   Auchnafree Hill

Ben Vorlich   Stuc a' Chroin
Beinn Each

Mountain Mountain Group	Approach Routes	Estate Name	Estate Ref	Refer to page
Schiehallion	From north-east and east	CROSSMOUNT	20/f	137
		KYNACHAN	20/g	137
		FOREST ENTERPRISE	20/a	136
	From south-east and south	GLENGOULANDIE	20/h	137
		GARTH	20/i	137
		INCHGARTH	20/k	138
	From north-west and west	WEST TEMPAR	20/e	137

Mountain Mountain Group	Approach Routes	Estate Name	Estate Ref	Refer to page
Carn Gorm Meall Garbh Creag Mhor Carn Mairg	From north-west	FOREST ENTERPRISE CORRIE CARIE	20/a 20/b	136 136
	From north	INNERHADDEN DALCHOSNIE WEST TEMPAR	20/c 20/d 20/e	137 137 137
	From west	INNERWICK	20/n	138
	From south	FOREST ENTERPRISE NORTH CHESTHILL	20/a 20/m	136 138
Ben Lawers Group	From north	RORO INVERINAIN SOUTH CHESTHILL	20/o 20/p 20/q	138 138 138
	From east	FOREST ENTERPRISE	20/a	136
	From south	BEN LAWERS	20/s	138
Meall nam Fuaran	From south	AUCHNAFREE	20/w	139
Creagan na Beinne	From north	ARDTALNAIG REMONY	20/u 20/v	139 139
	From south and east	AUCHNAFREE	20/w	139
Creag Uchdag	From north	WESTER TULLICH	20/t	139
	From south	INVERGELDIE	20/x	139
Ben Chonzie Auchnafree Hill	From north and north-east	AUCHNAFREE	20/w	139
	Glen Turret	GLENTURRET	20/z	139
	Glen Lednock	INVERGELDIE	20/x	139
Ben Vorlich Stuc a' Chroin Beinn Each	Ardvorlich	ARDVORLICH	20/bz	140
	Glen Ample	GLENAMPLE ESTATE	20/az	140
	Glen Artney	DRUMMOND ESTATES	20/y	139

Map 21T   Arrochar   Ben Lomond

Estate Reference	Estate Name	Estate Reference	Estate Name
21T/a	STUCKINDROIN	21T/e	GLENCROE
21T/b	STRONE ESTATE	21T/f	ARGYLL FOREST PARK
21T/c	SLOY	21T/g	FOREST ENTERPRISE
21T/d	INVERUGLAS	21T/h	BEN LOMOND

Mountains and Mountain Groups

Ben Vorlich

Ben Donich   The Brack

Arrochar Alps
Ben Arthur (The Cobbler)

Beinn Bheula

Ben Lomond

Beinn Ime

Map 21B   Arran

Estate Reference	Estate Name	Estate Reference	Estate Name
21B/a	DOUGARIE	21B/c	GOATFELL & GLEN ROSA
21B/b	ARRAN & SANNOX	21B/d	FOREST ENTERPRISE

Mountains and Mountain Groups

Beinn Bharrain

Goatfell

Caisteal Abhail   Cir Mhor
A' Chir   Beinn Tarsuinn

Beinn Bhreac

Mountain Mountain Group	Approach Routes	Estate Name	Estate Ref	Refer to page
Ben Vorlich	From north and east	STUCKINDROIN	21T/a	140
	Inveruglas	SLOY	21T/c	140
		INVERUGLAS	21T/d	140

Map on next page

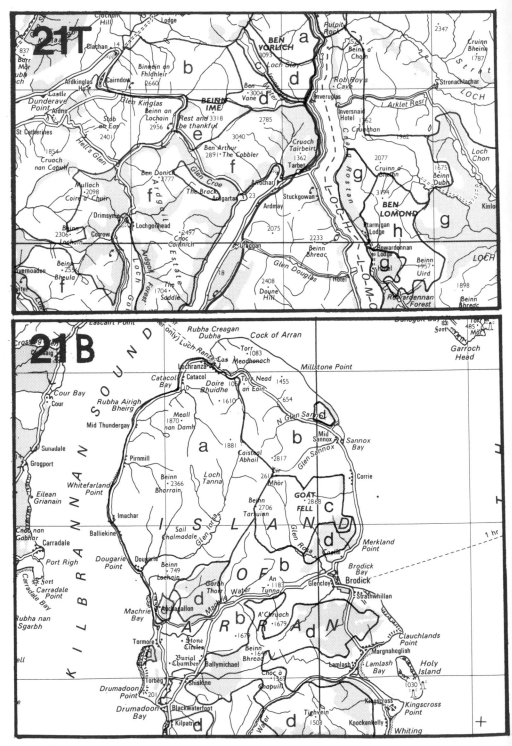

© Crown Copyright

Mountain Mountain Group	Approach Routes	Estate Name	Estate Ref	Refer to page
Arrochar Alps Ben Arthur (The Cobbler)	Inveruglas	SLOY INVERUGLAS	21T/c 21T/d	140 140
	Loch Long side and Rest and be Thankful	ARGYLL FOREST PARK	21T/f	140
Beinn Ime	Rest and be Thankful A83 and Butterbridge	GLENCROE	21T/e	140
Ben Donich The Brack	Loch Long Glen Croe and Rest and be Thankful	ARGYLL FOREST PARK	21T/f	140
Beinn Bheula	All approaches	ARGYLL FOREST PARK	21T/f	140
Ben Lomond	Rowardennan	BEN LOMOND	21T/h	141
	Lower slopes and from east	FOREST ENTERPRISE	21T/g	141
Beinn Bharrain	All routes	DOUGARIE	21B/a	141
Caisteal Abhail Cir Mhor A' Chir Beinn Tarsuinn	From north-east	ARRAN & SANNOX	21B/b	141
	From south-east	GOATFELL AND GLEN ROSA	21B/c	141
Goatfell	From north	ARRAN & SANNOX	21B/b	141
	From south	GOATFELL AND GLEN ROSA	21B/c	141
Beinn Bhreac	From north and south	FOREST ENTERPRISE	21B/d	141

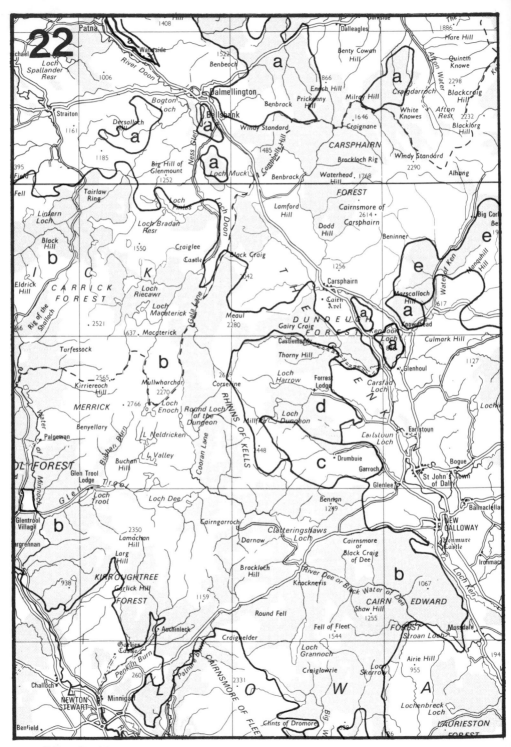

© Crown Copyright

Map 22   Galloway Hills

Estate Reference	Estate Name	Estate Reference	Estate Name
22/a	FOREST ENTERPRISE	22/d	FORREST ESTATE
22/b	GALLOWAY FOREST PARK	22/e	TILHILL ECONOMIC FORESTRY
22/c	GARROCH		

Mountains and Mountain Groups

Cairnsmore of Carsphairn	Merrick
Rhinns of Kells	Glen Trool Hills
Manquhill Hill	Cairnsmore of Fleet

Mountain Mountain Group	Approach Routes	Estate Name	Estate Ref	Refer to page
Rhinns of Kells	Rig of Clenrie	GARROCH	22/c	142
	Garroch Glen Forrest Glen	FORREST ESTATE	22/d	142
	Craigencallie GR 503 779	GALLOWAY FOREST PARK	22/b	141
Merrick Glen Trool Hills	All routes	GALLOWAY FOREST PARK	22/b	141
Cairnsmore of Fleet	Craignelder Craigronald Deer Park on A712 GR 523 732	GALLOWAY FOREST PARK	22/b	141
Manquhill Hill	Water of Ken	TILHILL ECONOMIC FORESTRY	22/e	142

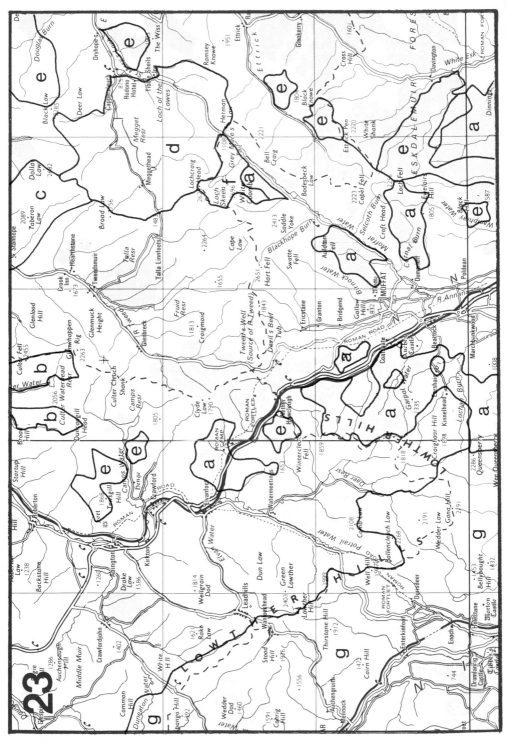

Map 23   Moffat Hills

Estate Reference	Estate Name	Estate Reference	Estate Name
23/a	FOREST ENTERPRISE	23/f	GREY MARE'S TAIL
23/b	CULTER ALLERS		WHITE COOMB AND
23/c	STANHOPE ESTATE		LOCH SKEEN
23/d	WEMYSS AND MARCH ESTATE	23/g	QUEENSBERRY ESTATE
23/e	TILHILL ECONOMIC FORESTRY		

Mountains and Mountain Groups

Hart Fell	White Coomb	Eskdalemuir Forest
Ettrick Hills		Lowther Hills

Mountain Mountain Group	Approach Routes	Estate Name	Estate Ref	Refer to page
Hart Fell White Coomb	Loch Skeen	GREY MARE'S TAIL WHITE COOMB AND LOCH SKEEN	23/f	143
		WEMYSS AND MARCH ESTATE	23/d	142
Ettrick Hills	Riskinhope Ettrick	WEMYSS AND MARCH ESTATE	23/d	142
Eskdalemuir Forest		TILHILL ECONOMIC FORESTRY	23/e	142
		FOREST ENTERPRISE	23/a	142
Lowther Hills	A74	FOREST ENTERPRISE	23/a	141
	Various approaches	QUEENSBERRY ESTATE	23/g	143

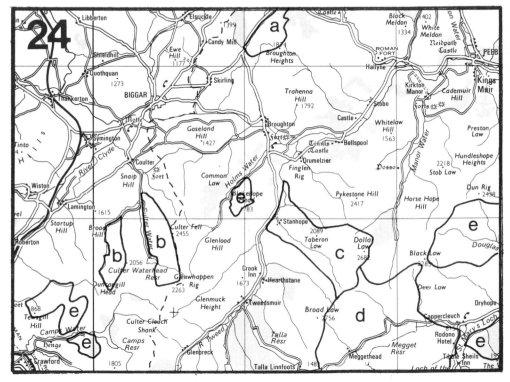

Map 24   Broad Law

Estate Reference	Estate Name	Estate Reference	Estate Name
24/a	LOCHURD	24/d	WEMYSS AND MARCH ESTATE
24/b	CULTER ALLERS		
24/c	STANHOPE ESTATE	24/e	TILHILL ECONOMIC FORESTRY

Mountains and Mountain Groups

Broughton Heights

Dollar Law

Culter Hills

Broad Law   Cramalt Craig

Mountain Mountain Group	Approach Routes	Estate Name	Estate Ref	Refer to page
Broughton Heights	Lochurd Farm	LOCHURD	24/a	143
Culter Hills	Various	TILHILL ECONOMIC FORESTRY	24/e	143
		CULTER ALLERS	24/b	143
Dollar Law	Stanhope Burn	STANHOPE ESTATE	24/c	143
	From south	WEMYSS AND MARCH ESTATE	24d	143
Broad Law Cramalt Craig	From south	WEMYSS AND MARCH ESTATE	24/d	143
	From north	STANHOPE ESTATE	24/c	143

List of Estates and Contact Addresses

Estate Ref	Estate Name	Contact	Estate Requests
1/a	RHICONICH Mr Richard Osborne Mr Gerald Osborne Lawn Farm Milton Lilbourne Pewsey Wilts	Graham Wild Ray Fish Rhiconich Hotel Rhiconich by Lairg Sutherland Tel 01971 521224	Please contact Rhiconich Hotel during stalking season
1/b	GUALIN ESTATE Gualin House By Lairg Sutherland IV27 4LE	Mr Duncan Shaw Keeper Tel 01971 521282	No parking at Gualin House Please park in quarry north of Lodge No bicycles Please keep dogs under control Check with Keeper during stalking season
1/c	BALNAKEIL Messrs Elliot Balnakeil House Balnakeil Durness by Lairg Sutherland	Balnakeil Farmhouse Tel 01971 511320	Dogs off leash not welcome Please contact at lambing time and stag stalking season
1/d	RISPOND & POLLA Mr & Mrs C Marsham Rispond Durness By Lairg Sutherland	Mr & Mrs C Marsham Rispond Durness Tel 01971 511224	No parking available at Polla Cottage
1/e	REAY FOREST Trustees of 2nd Duke of Westminster Estate Office Achfary by Lairg Sutherland	Estate Office Achfary by Lairg Sutherland Tel 01971 500221 Victor Anderson Head Stalker Ardchuillen Achfary Tel 01971 500223	No access by car to Lone Please park in the area provided near main road and at car park provided at bridge
1/f	STRATHMORE Mrs D J H Gow Pitscandly Forfar Angus	The Stalker Strathmore Altnaharra Tel 01549 411248	Route up from Mhuiseil Shed Please park in lay-by provided and not at cattle shed Kindly use the track

Estate Ref	Estate Name	Contact	Estate Requests
1/g	KINLOCH A W G Sykes Kinloch Lodge Tongue Sutherland	A Henderson The Stalker Tel 01847 611316	Parking only available on public highway
1/h	BEN LOYAL Count A W Knuth Loch Loyal Lodge Lairg Sutherland IV27 4AF	Loch Loyal Lodge Lairg Sutherland Tel 01847 611291 or 611220	
1/i	NORTH LOCHNAVER ESTATE North Lochnaver Estate Partnership per Finlayson Hughes 29 Barossa Place Perth PH1 5EP	David Horsburgh Tel 01641 561224	
1/k	ALTNAHARRA ESTATE Gray & Adams Ltd South Road Fraserburgh Aberdeenshire AB43 5HU	Malcolm Beaton Head Keeper Head Keeper's Cottage Altnaharra Estate Lairg Sutherland Tel 01549 411220	Car park by Vagastie bridge
1/m	MERKLAND Mr Robert Woods The Old Rectory Frilsham Nr Newbury Berkshire RG16 9XH	Mr Alan Walker Stalker Tel 01549 431222	
2/a	LOCH ASSYNT ESTATE Filmer-Sankey Discretionary Settlement per Assynt Estate Office Lochinver by Lairg Sutherland IV27 4JY	Stalker Tel 01571 822242 Estate Office Tel 01571 844203	Please use car park near summit of A849 (Skiag) road and access gate opposite
2/b	KYLESTROME Lady Mary Grosvenor Kylestrome Lodge Scourie by Lairg Sutherland IV27 4TL	Peter Allen Grieve Kylestrome Tel 01971 502220 or 502218	

Estate Ref	Estate Name	Contact	Estate Requests
2/c	REAY FOREST Trustees of 2nd Duke of Westminster Estate Office Achfary by Lairg Sutherland	Estate Office Achfary by Lairg Sutherland Tel 01971 500221 Victor Anderson Head Stalker Ardchuillen Achfary Tel 01971 500223	No access by car to Lone Please park in the area provided near main road and at car park provided at bridge
2/d	GLENCANISP AND DRUMRUNIE Glencanisp and Drumrunie Deer Forest Trust Assynt Estate Office Lochinver by Lairg Sutherland IV27 4JY	Stalker (Drumrunie) Tel 01854 666238 Stalker (South Inchnadamph) Tel 01571 822208 Stalker (Glencanisp) Tel 01571 844219	Leaflet available from Estate Office Tel 01571 844203
2/e	INCHNADAMPH GMW Vestey's Trust Assynt Estate Office Lochinver by Lairg Sutherland IV27 4JY	Stalker Tel 01571 822242 Estate Office Tel 01571 844203	Please use official car park west of Inchnadamph Hotel
2/f	MERKLAND Mr Robert Woods The Old Rectory Frilsham Nr Newbury Berkshire RG16 9XH	Mr Alan Walker Stalker Tel 01549 431222	
2/g	INVERCASSLEY Shop & Store Investments Ltd Burley House Bradford Road Burley-in-Wharfedale Ilkley West Yorkshire LS29 7DZ	Mr Brehmer South Cottage Rosehall Lairg Sutherland Tel 01549 441298	
2/h	DUCHALLY Balnagowan Castle Properties Ltd Balnagowan Kildary Ross-shire IV18 0NU	Mr T Coyle Estate Manager Tel 01862 843601	
2/i	INVERPOLLY Polly Estates Ltd Inverpolly Ullapool Ross-shire IV26 2YB	Estate Office Inverpolly Tel 01854 622452	Public car park

Estate Ref	Estate Name	Contact	Estate Requests
2/k	BENMORE J E M Vestey's Trust Assynt Estate Office Lochinver by Lairg Sutherland IV27 4JY	Stalker Tel 01854 666235 Estate Office Tel 01571 844203	Please park beside notice at south end of Loch Ailsh
2/m	BENMORE COIGACH Scottish Wildlife Trust c/o Finlayson Hughes 45 Church Street Inverness IV1 1DR	Warden John Smith North Keanchulish Ullapool Ross-shire IV26 2TW Tel 01854 612531	Car park at Culnacraig Contact Wildlife Warden for information
2/n	KEANCHULISH Mr L Bramall "Commanders Croft" Blughasary Strathkanaird Ullapool	Not required	Parking is available by a public park on the west side of the Drumrunie to Achiltibuie road near to Stac Pollaidh
2/o	FOREST ENTERPRISE Hilton of Embo Dornoch IV25 3PW	Tel 01862 810359	
3A/a	ALTNAHARRA ESTATE Gray & Adams Ltd South Road Fraserburgh Aberdeenshire AB43 5HU	Malcolm Beaton Head Keeper Head Keeper's Cottage Altnaharra Estate Lairg Sutherland Tel 01549 411220	Car park by Vagastie bridge
3A/b	CLEBRIG Mrs J Nicholson Clebrig Altnaharra Lairg Sutherland IV27 4VQ	D G MacKay Manager Clebrig Altnaharra Lairg Sutherland Tel 01549 411251	
3A/c	LOCH CHOIRE ESTATE Lord Joicey and Mr D A Knowles Loch Choire Lodge Kinbrace Sutherland KW11 6UD	A J Grant Loch Choire Kinbrace Sutherland Tel 01431 831222	

Estate Ref	Estate Name	Contact	Estate Requests
3A/d	FOREST ENTERPRISE Hilton of Embo Dornoch IV25 3PW	Tel 01862 810359	
3A/e	DALNESSIE ESTATE Ericht Farming Co Mr J V Ryan Mrs J V Ryan Milton of Drimmie Bridge of Cally Perthshire PH10 7JR	The Keeper Ian Hepburn Tel 01549 402287 (day) 01549 402435 (evening)	
3A/f	BEN ARMINE Ben Armine Estate Sutherland Estates Office Golspie Sutherland KW10 6RR	Lord Strathnaver Sutherland Estates Office Golspie Sutherland KW10 6RR Tel 01408 633268	
3B/a	DUNBEATH Dunbeath Estates Co Ltd per Finlayson Hughes 45 Church Street Inverness IV1 1DR	Lachie Geddes Tel 01382 566421	
3B/b	BRAEMORE The Wellbeck Estates Co Ltd Portland Estate Office Berriedale Caithness KW7 6HE	J Miller Braemore Keeper Keeper's House Braemore Tel 01593 731371	Please park by public call box at Braemore
3B/c	SUISGILL Mr E M Reeves Suisgill Estate Kildonan Helmsdale Sutherland KW8 6HY	The Stalker Tel 01831 431217	Dogs to be kept under close control
3B/d	LANGWELL The Wellbeck Estates Co Ltd Portland Estate Office Berriedale Caithness KW7 6HE	J Miller Braemore Keeper Keeper's House Braemore Tel 01593 731371	Please park by public call box at Braemore

Estate Ref	Estate Name	Contact	Estate Requests
3B/e	TORRISH Torrish Estate Co Ltd Torrish Helmsdale Sutherland	Head Keeper J Bain Tel 01431 821691	Ring J Bain
3B/f	KILDONAN Mrs M E A Clay Kildonan Lodge Helmsdale Sutherland KW8 6NY	Mr Grant Head Keeper Tel 01431 831263	
3B/g	CRAKAIG Mrs M Dudgeon Crakaig Helmsdale Sutherland		
4./a	INVERLAEL DEER FOREST Foich Estate	Mr A MacGillivray Keeper Tel 01854 655274	Cars should be left at the bottom of the private farm road and not taken through the field and forest
4/b	ALLADALE & DEANICH Richard Macaire per Finlayson Hughes 45 Church Street Inverness IV1 1DR	Iain Russell Tel 01463 224343	
4/c	FOREST FARM per Messrs Bowlts Chartered Surveyors Barnhill Pluscarden by Elgin Moray IV30 3TZ	Messrs Bowlts Chartered Surveyors Barnhill Pluscarden by Elgin Moray IV30 3TZ Tel 01343 890400 Fax 01343 890222	
4/d	GLENCALVIE Stonor Hotels Ltd per Messrs Bowlts Chartered Surveyors Barnhill Pluscarden by Elgin Moray IV30 3TZ	Messrs Bowlts Chartered Surveyors Barnhill Pluscarden by Elgin Moray IV30 3TZ Tel 01343 890400 Fax 01343 890222	

Estate Ref	Estate Name	Contact	Estate Requests
4/e	INVERLAEL c/o J Whitteridge Inverlael Loch Broom by Ullapool Ross-shire	Tel 01854 655262 or 655251	
4/f	BRAEMORE Mrs D Dowdeswell per Finlayson Hughes 45 Church Street Inverness IV1 1DR	C Gamble The Keeper Tel 01854 655374	PLEASE do not use estate drive Cars to be left at car park Use gate at east end of car park for access to hill
4/g	INVERBROOM The Hon E M W Robson per Finlayson Hughes 45 Church Street Inverness IV1 1DR	The Keeper Tel 01854 655252	
4/h	FOICH ESTATE	W J Mackenzie Stalker Tel 01854 655232	
4/i	WEST FANNICH Mr Pat Wilson Loanleven Almondbank Perth PH1 3NF	Ronnie Ross Tel 01445 720223	
4/k	FANNICH W Baron van Dedem 1 Trumpeters House Old Palace Yard Richmond Surrey TW9 1PD	Norrie Matheson Tel 01997 414318	Please use road on north side of Loch Fannich
4/m	LOCHLUICHART Lochluichart Estate Company Limited per Messrs Bowlts Chartered Surveyors Barnhill Pluscarden by Elgin Moray IV30 3TZ	Messrs Bowlts Chartered Surveyors Barnhill Pluscarden by Elgin Moray IV30 3TZ Tel 01343 890400 Fax 01343 890222	

Estate Ref	Estate Name	Contact	Estate Requests
4/n	STRATHVAICH ESTATE Strathvaich Partners Strathvaich Lodge Ross-shire	Ian Bennett The Keeper Tel 01997 455226	All Estate roads are strictly PRIVATE All cars to be left on the main road or the parking area at the bottom of the Strathvaich drive
4/o	KILDERMORIE Mrs and Mrs I A Duncan Ardross by Alness Easter Ross IV17 0YH	The Head Stalker Tel 01349 884178	No access for vehicles including bicycles without permission Walkers please use paths and respect grouse and red deer seasons Dogs off lead not welcome
4/p	FOREST ENTERPRISE Hilton of Embo Dornoch IV25 3PW	Tel 01862 810359	
4/q	WYVIS	Mr Gordon Beattie Stalker Tel 01349 830405	Parking in lay-by outside entrance gate at Gate Lodge Please confirm routes in advance with the stalker during the stalking season in September and October
4/r	FOREST ENTERPRISE Smithton Inverness IV1 2NL	Tel 01463 791575	
4/s	CORRIEMOILLIE Fridays Cranbook Ltd c/o D Shand Station Road Dingwall	Tel 01349 863620	
5/a	TOURNAIG Lady Horlick Tournaig Poolewe by Achnasheen Ross-shire	Donald MacLean Tournaig Farm Cottage Tel 01445 781295	For permission to camp ask either Mr MacLean or Lady Horlick

Estate Ref	Estate Name	Contact	Estate Requests
5/b	LITTLE GRUINARD Mr P Van Vlissingen Ardlair Ross-shire	Fishing Ghillie Mr George Mackenzie Tel 01445 731215	
5/c	GRUINARD Hon Mrs A G Maclay Gruinard Estate Laide by Achnasheen Ross-shire IV22 2NQ	Estate Manager Mr Grant MacDougall Green Cottage Gruinard Tel 01445 731240	
5/d	DUNDONNELL A S Roger Dundonnell Estate by Garve Ross-shire	Estate Manager Tel 01854 633219	
5/e	GAIRLOCH J A Mackenzie Estates Office Conon Bridge Ross-shire IV7 8AL	Roger McDonald Estate Office Gairloch IV21 2AJ Tel 01445 712378 (day) 712116 (evening)	
5/f	ARDLAIR/ FISHERFIELD/ LETTEREWE Mr P Van Vlissingen Ardlair Ross-shire	The Stalker Kernsary Tel 01445 781215 or The Stalker Kinlochewe Tel 01445 760302	Please use existing paths during approach
5/g	EILEAN DARACH Col Dunphie Cloquhat Bridge of Cally Perthshire PH10 7JP	The Keeper Tel 01854 633203	Please use the gate beside the pair of cedar cottages 600 yards east of Dundonnell Hotel for access to main An Teallach path
5/h	INVERBROOM The Hon E M W Robson per Finlayson Hughes 45 Church Street Inverness IV1 1DR	Tel 01854 655252	
5/i	FOICH ESTATE	W J Mackenzie Stalker Tel 01854 655232	

Estate Ref	Estate Name	Contact	Estate Requests
5/k	GRUDIE & TALLADALE P J H Wills Kirkham Farm Lower Slaughter Cheltenham Glos	Tel 01445 760259	Call at cottage in stalking season Please avoid eroding screes
5/m	KINLOCHEWE Mr Pat Wilson Loanleven Almondbank Perth PH1 3NF	Ronnie Ross Tel 01445 720223	
5/n	WEST FANNICH Mr Pat Wilson Loanleven Almondbank Perth PH1 3NF	Ronnie Ross Tel 01445 720223	
5/o	DIABAIG Paul Nicholson 23 Diabaig Torridon Achnasheen Wester Ross	Mr D Beaton 1 Wester Alligin Torridon by Achnasheen Ross-shire IV22 2HD Tel 01445 791201	Part of Gairloch conservation unit for Deer Management
5/p	BEINN EIGHE NATIONAL NATURE RESERVE Scottish Natural Heritage Fraser Darling House 9 Culduthel Road Inverness IV2 4AG	Anancaun Visitor Centre Kinlochewe by Achnasheen Ross-shire IV22 2PA Tel 01445 760254	
5/q	TORRIDON National Trust for Scotland 5 Charlotte Square Edinburgh EH2 4DL	The Ranger The Mains Torridon Tel 01445 791221	Car parks at entrance to both Coire Dubh and Coire Mhic Nobuil
5/r	LOCH ROSQUE Mr Pat Wilson Loanleven Almondbank Perth PH1 3NF	Ronnie Ross Tel 01445 720223	

Estate Ref	Estate Name	Contact	Estate Requests
6/a	APPLECROSS* The Applecross Estate Trust per L Lumsden Administrator Wester Altourie Abriachan Inverness-shire IV3 6LB	Stalker (1) K Griffin The Kennels Applecross Strathcarron Tel 01520 744247 Stalker (2) D Abraham Russel Kishorn Strathcarron Tel 01520 733249	Please keep Mr Griffin informed of planned routes*
6/b	KINLOCH* Richard Munday Esq Kinloch Shieldaig Strathcarron Ross-shire	Richard or Claire Munday Kinloch Shieldaig Strathcarron Ross-shire Tel 01520 755206	
6/c	BEN SHIELDAIG* The Hon Hugh Tollemache Sandbourne House Earl's Groome Worcs WR8 9DG		
6/d	COULDORAN* Mr & Mrs M Pattinson Couldoran Kishorn Strathcarron Ross-shire IV54 8UY	Mr & Mrs Pattinson Couldoran Kishorn Strathcarron Tel 01520 733227	
6/e	BEN DAMPH ESTATE* Messrs T D Gray & D N Carr-Smith Gt Yeldham Hall Halstead Essex	Alistair Holmes 2 Fuaran Torridon Wester Ross Tel 01445 791252	Please do not leave clearly defined footpaths during the stag stalking season 7 Sept- 20 Oct unless agreed with estate
6/f	COULIN* The Hon P R Smith's Discretionary Trust per Finlayson Hughes 29 Barossa Place Perth PH1 5EP	Head Stalker Coulin Estate Kinlochewe Tel 01445 760383	Car park at Coire Dubh and entrance to estate off Kinlochewe/ Torridon road No access for motor cars without prior permission

South West Ross Deer Management Group Member
For Achnashellach and Glencarron & Glenuig this applies to the areas north of the A890

Estate Ref	Estate Name	Contact	Estate Requests
6/g	KINLOCHEWE Mr Pat Wilson Loanleven Almondbank Perth PH1 3NF	Ronnie Ross Tel 01445 720223	
6/h	LOCH ROSQUE Mr Pat Wilson Loanleven Almondbank Perth PH1 3NF	Ronnie Ross Tel 01445 720223	
6/i	LOCHCARRON*	Mr & Mrs Pattinson Couldoran Kishorn Strathcarron Tel 01520 733227	
6/k	GLENMORE* Fred Booker Deffer House High Hoyland Barnsley South Yorkshire S75 4AY	The Keeper Glenmor Kishorn Strathcarron Ross-shire Tel 01520 733259	
6/m	TULLICH* R Chambers Esq Tullich Strathcarron Ross-shire	Mr & Mrs Pattinson Couldoran Kishorn Strathcarron Tel 01520 733227	
6/n	NEW KELSO* Conon Brae Farms Torgorm Conon Bridge Dingwall Ross-shire IV7 8DN	S Shaun Macdonald Tel 01349 864419	
6/o	FIONNARAICH* J Fooks/ Mrs S Block Woodgate House Beckley Sussex TN31 6UH		Please do not leave well defined footpaths in the stalking season Sept to mid-Oct unless a route is agreed with the estate
6/p	ACHNASHELLACH* Major M T N H Wills Misarden Park Stroud Glos GL6 7JA	Mr C Mackenzie Stalker Craig Cottage Achnashellach Tel 01520 766266	

South West Ross Deer Management Group Member
For Achnashellach and Glencarron & Glenuig this applies to the areas north of the A890

Estate Ref	Estate Name	Contact	Estate Requests
6/q	FOREST ENTERPRISE Strathoich Fort Augustus Inverness-shire PH32 4BT	Tel 01320 366322 Fax 01320 366581	
6/r	GLENCARRON & GLENUIG* Glencarron Estate Partnership Glencarron Lodge by Strathcarron Wester Ross	Brian Watson West Cottage Glencarron Lodge by Strathcarron Tel 01520 766275	
6/s	LEDGOWAN* James R Ruggles-Brise Ledgowan Achnasheen Ross-shire IV22 2EH	Tommy Ross Ledgowan Estate Tel 01445 720209	
6/t	STRATHCONON Kirbi Estates Ltd Strathconon House Strathconon Muir of Ord Ross-shire IV6 7QQ	P Smith Head Stalker Achlorachan House Strathconon Tel 01997 477230	Vehicles should not be parked so as to block hill tracks Take notice of signs erected at access to hill land
6/u	SCARDROY Burnden Park Investments	The Head Stalker Tel 01997 477267	
6/v	ATTADALE E A Macpherson Attadale Strathcarron Wester Ross IV54 8YX	T Watson Stalker's House Attadale Tel 01520 722308	
6/w	WEST MONAR C S R Stroyan Bridgend of Teith Doune Perthshire FK16 8AD	Mr D Lippe Stalker Pait Bheag Monar Tel 01463 761267	Only approachable on foot Please use paths along the bottom of the glens during access
6/x	EAST MONAR David C R Allen East Monar Struy Beauly Ross-shire	Stephen Potter Stalker's Cottage East Monar Tel 01463 761210	

South West Ross Deer Management Group Member
For Achnashellach and Glencarron & Glenuig this applies to the areas north of the A890

Estate Ref	Estate Name	Contact	Estate Requests
6/y	KILLILAN Smech Properties Inverinate Estate Office Kyle Ross-shire IV40 8HB	Mr David Glover Estate Manager The Square Inverinate Tel 01599 511303/ 250	
6/z	PAIT C S R Stroyan Bridgend of Teith Doune Perthshire FK16 8AD	Mr D Lippe Stalker Pait Bheag Monar Tel 01463 761267	Only approachable on foot Please use paths along the bottom of the glens during access
6/az	BRAULEN Bidwells Chartered Surveyors Etive House Beechwood Business Park Inverness IV2 3BW	The Gatekeeper Tel 01463 761260 or SNH Warden Tel 01349 865333	Glen Strathfarrar access April-October The entrance gate is con- trolled by gatekeepers No vehicle access on Tuesdays and Sunday mornings November to March Application for vehicle access should be made in advance to the gatekeepers SNH Warden or the estate
6/bz	WEST BENULA Smech Properties Inverinate Estate Office Kyle Ross-shire IV40 8HB	Estate Manager The Square Inverinate Tel 01599 511303/ 250	
6/cz	EAST BENULA		
6/dz	COZAC Sir John & Mr Anthony Fuller	Donald Fraser Estate Stalker Carrie Glen Cannich by Beauly IV4 7LX Tel 01456 415339	
7T/a	STRATHCONON Kirkbi Estates Ltd Strathconon House Strathconon Muir of Ord Ross-shire IV6 7QQ	P Smith Head Stalker Achlorachan House Strathconon Tel 01997 477230	Vehicles should not be parked so as to block hill tracks Take notice of signs erected at access to hill land

Estate Ref	Estate Name	Contact	Estate Requests
7T/b	SCATWELL ESTATE	Mike Watt Tel 01997 466221	Phone between Aug- Oct Please shut gates
7T/c	FAIRBURN & CORRIEHALLIE R W K Stirling Arcan Muir of Ord IV6 7UL	R W K Stirling Tel 01997 433273 or Keith Wilkinson Tel 01997 433243	Walkers are very welcome It would be helpful if between 20 Sept -15 Oct Sundays excepted access to hill ground is restricted to the road up to the Orrin Dam During hind culling 21 Oct - Christmas in the interests of public safety please use hill paths unless contact has been made with the estate No litter please
7T/d	BRAULEN Bidwells Chartered Surveyors Etive House Beechwood Business Park Inverness IV2 3BW	The Gatekeeper Tel 01463 761360 or SNH Warden Tel 01349 865333	Glen Strathfarrar access April-October The entrance gate is con- trolled by gatekeepers No vehicle access on Tuesdays and Sunday mornings November to March Application for vehicle access should be made in advance to the gatekeepers SNH Warden or the estate
7T/e	STRUY per CAMS Ltd 59 Bonnygate Cupar Fife KY15 4BY	Henry Bain Stalker Struy Tel 01463 761276	
7T/f	CULLIGRAN C Frank Spencer-Nairn Culligran House Struy Beauly Inverness-shire IV4 7JX	C Frank Spencer-Nairn Tel 01463 761285 or The Gatekeeper Tel 01463 761260 or SNH Warden Tel 01349 865333	Parking at Inchmore near Glen Strathfarrar entrance gate Glen Strathfarrar access as for BRAULEN

Estate Ref	Estate Name	Contact	Estate Requests
7T/g	ERCHLESS The Hon E M W Robson per Finlayson Hughes 45 Church Street Inverness IV1 1DR	The Keeper Tel 01463 761205	
7T/h	FARLEY ESTATE	Finlay M Macrae Tel 01349 864987	Please take note of the information on the signs and make contact in the stag stalking season
7T/i	COZAC Sir John & Mr Anthony Fuller	Donald Fraser Estate Stalker Carrie Glen Cannich by Beauly IV4 7LX Tel 01456 415339	
7T/k	BALMORE Sir John & Mr Anthony Fuller	Donald Fraser Estate Stalker Carrie Glen Cannich by Beauly IV4 7LX Tel 01456 415339	
7T/m	FOREST ENTERPRISE Strathoich Fort Augustus PH32 4BT	Tel 01320 366322 Fax 01320 366581	
7T/n	BEAUFORT AND ESKADALE per Finlayson Hughes 45 Church Street Inverness IV1 1DR	Neil Lyon Tel 01456 476250	
7B/a	INVERINATE Smech Properties Ltd Inverinate Estate Office Kyle Ross-shire IV40 8HB	Mr David Glover Estate Manager The Square Inverinate Tel 01599 511303/ 250	
7B/b	GLOMACH Smech Properties Ltd Inverinate Estate Office Kyle Ross-shire IV40 8HB	Mr David Glover Estate Manager The Square Inverinate Tel 01599 511303/ 250	

Estate Ref	Estate Name	Contact	Estate Requests
7B/c	WEST BENULA Smech Properties Ltd Inverinate Estate Office Kyle Ross-shire IV40 8HB	Mr David Glover Estate Manager The Square Inverinate Tel 01599 511303/ 250	
7B/d	EAST BENULA		
7B/e	KINTAIL National Trust for Scotland 5 Charlotte Square Edinburgh EH2 4DU	NTS Ranger Morvich Tel 01599 511219	
7B/f	WEST AFFRIC National Trust for Scotland 5 Charlotte Square Edinburgh EH2 4DU	NTS Ranger Morvich Tel 01599 511219	
7B/g	LOCH AFFRIC ESTATE per Finlayson Hughes 45 Church Street Inverness IV1 1DR	Head Keeper Ronald Buchan Tel 01465 415350	Prior notice to Head Keeper Areas where stalking being done to be avoided during season Dogs to be leashed
7B/h	FOREST ENTERPRISE Strathoich Fort Augustus PH32 4BT	Tel 01320 366322 Fax 01320 366581	
7B/i	WESTER GUISACHAN R A K G Kwint		
7B/k	CEANNACROC ESTATE Glenmoriston Inverness-shire IV3 6YN	Tel/Fax 01320 340246	Tel/ Fax contact must be made in the stalking season 1 Sept - 25 Oct
7B/m	CORRIELAIR ESTATE J D Brown Battleby Farm Redgorton Perth	Tel 01738 828573	

Estate Ref	Estate Name	Contact	Estate Requests
7B/n	GLENSHIEL & CLUANIE Burton Property Trustees Dochfour Estate Office Dochgarroch Inverness IV3 6JP	Iain Campbell Estate Manager Shiel House Tel 01599 511282	
8T/a	EILEANREACH		
8T/b	ARNISDALE J H Richmond-Watson Wakefield Lodge Potterspury Northants	J H Richmond-Watson Tel 01327 811218 or 01599 522229	Parking at Corran
8T/c	KINTAIL National Trust for Scotland 5 Charlotte Square Edinburgh EH2 4DU	NTS Ranger Morvich Tel 01599 511219	
8T/d	GLENSHIEL & CLUANIE Burton Property Trustees Dochfour Estate Office Dochgarroch Inverness IV3 6JP	Iain Campbell Estate Manager Shiel House Tel 01599 511282	
8T/e	KINLOCH HOURN Henry C Birkbeck Estate Office Westacre King's Lynn Norfolk PE32 1UB	Donald Cameron Stalker's Cottage Kinloch Hourn Invergarry Tel 01809 511236	Car park at Loch Hourn head
8T/f	KNOYDART Titaghur PLC	The Estate Office Tel 01687 462331	
8T/g	LI & COIRE DHORRCAIL John Muir Trust Ltd 12 Wellington Place Leith Edinburgh EH6 7EQ	Keith Miller Strathaird Broadford Isle of Skye IV49 9AX Tel 01471 866260	

Estate Ref	Estate Name	Contact	Estate Requests
8T/h	BARRISDALE R and J Gordon Lude Farm Blair Atholl Perthshire PH18 5TS	Estate Manager When at Barrisdale	Please camp at Kinloch Hourn camp site or Barrisdale camp site Contact Estate Manager when at Barrisdale between end of August and mid-October if walking off paths Small charge for use of Barrisdale bothy
8T/i	WESTER GLENQUOICH Captain A D Gordon	Tel 01809 511220	Camping only at designated camp sites at Kinloch Hourn GR950066 and Kingie GR102013 Please keep to signed routes and no climbing between 1 Sept and 10 Oct due to deer stalking unless an alternative has been agreed with the stalker
8T/k	KILCHOAN per West Highland Estates Office 33 High Street Fort William Inverness-shire PH33 6DJ	West Highland Estates Office Tel 01397 702433 or A Harris (stalker) Tel 01687 462724	
8T/m	CAMUSRORY J G Crosthwaithe-Eyre The Estate Office Warrens Bramshaw Hampshire SO43 7JH Tel 01703 812339/ 813954	The Manager Camusrory Wireless Telephone 01687 462342	Walkers are always welcome but please camp only at Sourlies bothy and use paths during the period mid-August to mid-October unless an alternative agreed
8T/n	GLENDESSARY DEER FOREST Inc Glen Pean and Gleann-a-Chaorainn Mr Robert Schmitt	A Walker Stalker Glendessary Lodge by Spean Bridge Inverness-shire Tel 01397 712463	No parking available at Glendessary Lodge

Estate Ref	Estate Name	Contact	Estate Requests
8T/o	NORTH MORAR ESTATE I R S Bond Swordlands Lodge North Morar Mallaig PH40 4PE	Stalker Alec Mackay Alt Mhor Bracora Mallaig Tel 01687 462056	Walkers are requested to use lochside routes only during mid-August and mid-October unless an alternative has been agreed with the stalker
8T/p	KINGIE I & H Brown Ltd Dunkeld Road Perth	John Cameron Stalker's Cottage Kingie Invergarry Tel 01809 511261	
8T/q	LOCHIEL ESTATE Achnacarry North Forest D A Cameron Yr of Lochiel Achnacarry Spean Bridge Inverness-shire	Stalker on land to north of Loch Arkaig Tel 01397 712709	Walkers are welcome at most times and are requested to remain on rights of way during the period mid-August to mid October unless an alternative has been agreed with the stalker for the appropriate area
8B/a	FOREST ENTERPRISE Torlundy Fort William PH33 6SW	Tel 01397 702184	
8B/b	ABERCHALDER Miss Jean Ellice Taigh-an-Lianach Aberchalder Farm Invergarry PH35 4HN	Miss Jean Ellice Tel 01809 501287	Parking by prior arrangement only
8B/c	CULACHY H G Biggs Tarff House Culachy Fort Augustus PH32 4BY	Keeper's Cottage Culachy Tel 01320 366732	Parking on public road only Please use "Wade's Road" pedestrian right of way during deer culling season 1 Aug - 1 Feb unless an alternative has been agreed

Estate Ref	Estate Name	Contact	Estate Requests
8B/d	LOCHIEL ESTATE D A Cameron Yr of Lochiel Achnacarry Spean Bridge Inverness-shire	Stalker on land to north of Loch Arkaig Tel 01397 712709 Stalker on land to south of Loch Arkaig Tel 01397 712714	Walkers are welcome at most times and are requested to remain on rights of way during the period mid-August to mid- October unless an alternative has been agreed with the stalker for the appropriate area
8B/e	BRAEROY Mr B K D Buckle Dairy Farm Office Semer Ipswich Suffolk IP7 6RA	The Stalker Braeroy Roybridge Tel 01397 71220 or 01397 712887 (Home)	Parking in lay-by close to footbridge in Glen Roy
8B/f	GLEN GLOY ESTATE	Estate Manager Lowbridge Glen Gloy Spean Bridge Inverness-shire PH34 4DX Tel 01397 712637	
8B/g	GLEN ROY NATIONAL NATURE RESERVE Scottish Natural Heritage NW Region Fraser Darling House 9 Culduthel Road Inverness IV2 4AG	North Lochaber Area Officer Scottish Natural Heritage The Governor's House The Parade Fort William PH33 6BA Tel 01397 704716	
8B/h	GLENSPEAN Mrs E J Macdonald Ardslignish Ardnamurchan Argyll PH36 4JG	Mrs E J Macdonald Tel 01972 500700	
9/a	ARISAIG Amphill Investments Ltd per Brodies WS Solicitors 15 Atholl Crescent Edinburgh EH3 8HA	Mr J Colston Tel 01687 450609	

Estate Ref	Estate Name	Contact	Estate Requests
9/b	MEOBLE & LETTERMORAR Mr M Z de Ferranti Meoble Lodge Morar Inverness-shire PH40 4PG	Mrs C M Davies D F M Bangor Gwynedd Tel 01248 370370	
9/c	GLENFINNAN M R Warren per Tilhill Economic Forestry Old Hydro Building Bank Street Fort William PH33 6AY	The Stalker Tel 01397 722203	
9/d	GLEANN FIONNLIGHE Tilhill Economic Forestry Old Hydro Building Bank Street Fort William PH33 6AY	Miller Harris Tilhill Economic Forestry Old Hydro Building Bank Street Fort William PH33 6AY Tel 01397 705101	No vehicles please Please ensure gates are kept closed Stiles in situ for access
9/e	LOCHIEL ESTATE Achnacarry South Forest Achdalieu Deer Forest D A Cameron Yr of Lochiel Achnacarry Spean Bridge Inverness-shire	e(n) Achnacarry South Forest Stalker Tel 01397 712714 e(s) Achdalieu Deer Forest Stalker Tel 01397 772296	Walkers are welcome at most times and are asked to use rights of way from mid-Aug to mid-Oct unless an alternative has been agreed with the stalker for the area
9/f	INVERAILORT ESTATE* c/o Hugh A Maclaren Castlehill Farm Office Inchture Perthshire PH14 9SH	Tel 01687 470234	
9/g	GLEN MAMA	Mr R Maclaren (Stalker) Tel 01687 470207	
9/h	ROSHVEN* Captain J A P Forbes Marino Lodge Lochailort	Colin Surnam c/o Post Office Lochailort by Fort William Inverness-shire Tel 01687 470200	

* Moidart Deer Management Group Member

Estate Ref	Estate Name	Contact	Estate Requests
9/i	WEST ROSHVEN* Mrs P Blackburn Kemble Roshven by Lochailort	Tel 01687 470241	Please avoid the stalking season unless contact has been made
9/k	GLENUIG* Mrs J M Llewellyn Samalaman House Glenuig Lochailort Inverness-shire PH38 4NG	Tel 01687 470229	Walkers are requested to use coastline or paths between 1 and 20 October unless an alternative has been agreed with the estate
9/m	KINLOCHMOIDART* Mrs N Stewart	Tel 01967 431609	
9/n	GLENMOIDART* J Lees-Millais Esq Glenmoidart House by Lochailort	The Stalker M MacLean Garden Cottage Tel 01967 431254	
9/o	GLENALADALE* H Cheape Esq Shlatach Glenfinnan	The Stalker D MacAulay Shlatach Tel 01397 722241	
9/p	LOCHSHIEL* The Westminster (Liverpool) Trust per West Highland Estates Office 33 High Street Fort William Inverness-shire PH33 6DJ	G Shankland Keeper's Cottage Dorlin Acharacle Argyll Tel 01967 431618	
9/q	EILEAN SHONA* R Devereaux Esq	Mr and Mrs Lewis Tel 01967 431249	
9/r	SHONA BEAG* Invermoidart Acharacle Argyll PH36 4LR	S Lindsay Tel 01967 431225	
9/s	KYLESWOOD*	Tel 01967 431662	

* Moidart Deer Management Group Member

Estate Ref	Estate Name	Contact	Estate Requests
9/t	FOREST ENTERPRISE Torlundy Fort William PH33 6SW	Tel 01397 702184/ 5	
9/u	CONA GLEN J Guthrie Esq per West Highland Estates Office 33 High Street Fort William Inverness-shire PH33 6DJ	I L M Hislop West Highland Estates Office 33 High Street Fort William Tel 01397 702433 or D Kennedy (Stalker) Tel 01855 841304	
9/v	ARDGOUR Executors of Miss MacLean of Ardgour Ardgour House Ardgour by Fort William	R M MacLean of Ardgour Sallachan Farm Ardgour Tel 01855 841247	Footpath through Glen Gour to Strontian Please remain on paths between 1 Sept and 20 Oct unless an alternative route has been agreed with the estate
9/w	INVERSANDA	The Manager Inversanda Estate Ardgour PH53 7AD Tel 01855 841305 or 841275	Please ask at Inversanda House during stalking September October and January
9/x	SUNART S O A E F D* Pentland House, 47 Robb's Loan Edinburgh EH14 1TW		
9/y	RESIPOLE WOODLANDS Tilhill Economic Forestry Old Hydro Building Bank Street Fort William PH33 6AY	Miller Harris Tilhill Economic Forestry Old Hydro Building Bank Street Fort William Tel 01397 705101	

* Scottish Office Agriculture Environment & Fisheries Department

Estate Ref	Estate Name	Contact	Estate Requests
10T/a	NORTH HARRIS ESTATE Jonathan Bulmer Amhuinnsuidhe Castle North Harris Western Isles HS3 3AS	Head Stalker Roddie Macleod Tel 01859 560232	The area west of the broken line is an SSSI and a Special Protection Area Please exercise discretion during the nesting and stalking seasons If in doubt contact the Head Stalker
10B/a	KILMUIR S O A E F D* Pentland House 47 Robb's Loan Edinburgh EH14 1TW	S O A E F D Estates Office Portree Skye IV51 9DH Tel 01478 612516	
10B/b	SCORRYBRECK S O A E F D* Pentland House 47 Robb's Loan Edinburgh EH14 1TW	S O A E F D Estates Office Portree Skye IV51 9DH Tel 01478 612516	
10/B/c	STORR FOREST The Highland Council	Roger Miket Area Cultural & Leisure Manager Tigh-na-Sgire Portree Isle of Skye IV51 9EP Tel 01478 613827	Public access welcomed
11/a	BRACADALE S O A E F D* Pentland House 47 Robb's Loan Edinburgh EH14 1TW	S O A E F D Estates Office Portree Skye IV51 9DH Tel 01478 612516	
11/b	BRAE EYNORT CROFT	John McDiarmid Tel 01478 640252	
11/c	FOREST ENTERPRISE Strathoich Fort Augustus Inverness-shire PH32 4BT	Tel 01320 366322 Fax 01320 366581	

* Scottish Office Agriculture Environment & Fisheries Department

Estate Ref	Estate Name	Contact	Estate Requests
11/d	MACLEOD ESTATE John MacLeod of MacLeod Dunvegan Skye	Hugh MacRae Glen Brittle Tel 01478 640335 or Camp Site Manager Tel 01478 640404	General camping at Glen Brittle camp site
11/e	SCONSER Mrs F Campbell Sconser Lodge Sconser Isle of Skye	Tel 01478 650232	
11/f	STRATHAIRD John Muir Trust Ltd 12 Wellington Place Leith Edinburgh EH6 7EQ	Keith Miller Strathaird Broadford Isle of Skye IV49 9AX Tel 01471 866260	
11/g	TORRIN John Muir Trust Ltd 12 Wellington Place Leith Edinburgh EH6 7EQ	Keith Miller Strathaird Broadford Isle of Skye IV49 9AX Tel 01471 866260	
11/h	RUM Scottish Natural Heritage Fraser Darling House 9 Culduthel Road Inverness IV2 4AG	Reserve Manager Isle of Rum Tel 01687 462026	Visitors intending to stay overnight should contact the Reserve Manager beforehand to secure accommodation Daily information board should be consulted
12T/a	BENMORE ESTATE	West Highland Estates Office 21 Argyll Square Oban PA34 4AT Tel 01631 563617 or Knock House Tel 01680 300356	

Estate Ref	Estate Name	Contact	Estate Requests
12T/b	GLENFORSA The Trustees of Glenforsa Estate c/o Finlayson Hughes 29 Barossa Place Perth PH1 5EP	Finlayson Hughes Tel 01738 625134	
12T/c	FOREST ENTERPRISE Millpark Road Oban Argyll PA34 4NH	Tel 01631 566155	
12T/d	TOROSAY Mr C James Torosay Craignure PA65 6AY	Estate Office Craignure Tel 01680 812421	In winter months please leave word at Estate Office Preferred route via Television Mast Road
12T/e	BURG National Trust for Scotland 5 Charlotte Square Edinburgh EH2 4DU	Regional Factor Albany Chambers Albany Street Oban Argyll Tel 01631 570000	
12T/f	ARDVERGNISH	Mr Angus Cheape Langley-Taylor 10 Great Stuart Street Edinburgh EH3 7TN Tel 0131 2200576	
12T/g	LOCHBUIE John Corbett Lochbuie House	James Corbett Laggan Farm Lochbuie Tel 01680 814214	
12T/h	DERERACH Mr and Mrs J Walton per Tilhill Economic Forestry Old Hydro Building Bank Street Fort William PH33 6AY	Miller Harris Tilhill Economic Forestry Old Hydro Building Bank Street Fort William Tel 01397 705101	

Estate Ref	Estate Name	Contact	Estate Requests
12B/a	TARBERT ESTATE The Viscount Astor Ginge Manor Wantage Oxon OX12 8QT	Gordon Muir Gatehouse Isle of Jura Tel 01496 820207	
12B/b	INVER Inver Farmers	Stalker Donald Darroch Tel 01496 820223	
12B/c	FOREST ESTATE Lord Vestey and Hon M Vestey	Head Stalker Dave Mack Forest Lodge Isle of Jura Tel 01496 820332	
12B/d	ARDFIN Mr A W A Riley-Smith	Head Stalker William Macdonald Tel 01496 820396	
13/a	FOREST ENTERPRISE Smithton Inverness IV1 2NL	Tel 01463 791575	
13/b	INSHRIACH/ INVERESHIE Cairngorms NNR Scottish Natural Heritage Achantoul Aviemore Inverness-shire PH22 1QD	D Duncan Area Officer SNH Achantoul Aviemore Tel 01479 810477	
13/c	ROTHIEMURCHUS John Grant of Rothiemurchus Rothiemurchus Estate Office by Aviemore PH22 1QH	Countryside Ranger Service Visitor Centre Inverdruie by Aviemore Tel 01479 810858	Preferred access to Braeriach by Lairig Ghru Sron na Lairige or Gleann Einich/ Coire Dhondail
13/d	GLENMORE The Queen's Forest FOREST ENTERPRISE Smithton Inverness IV1 2NL	The Glenmore Visitor Centre Tel 01479 861220 or Tel 01463 791575	
13/e	ABERNETHY FOREST RESERVE RSPB Forest Lodge Nethybridge Inverness-shire PH25 3EF	Desmond Dugan Warden Forest Lodge Nethybridge Inverness-shire PH25 3EF Tel 01479 821409	

Estate Ref	Estate Name	Contact	Estate Requests
13/f	GLENAVON (INCHRORY) Bidwells Chartered Surveyors Etive House Beechwood Park Inverness IV2 3BW	Tel 01463 715585	
13/g	ALLARGUE Corgarff Strathdon Aberdeenshire AB36 8YP	F M K Tuck Tel 019756 51452 or Keeper Tel 019756 51448	
13/h	DELNADAMPH The Balmoral Estates' Trustees Balmoral Estate Office Balmoral Ballater Aberdeenshire AB35 5TB		
13/i	GLENFESHIE Will Woodlands per West Highland Estates Office 33 High Street Fort William PH33 6DJ	A Dempster Head Stalker Glenfeshie Kincraig Tel 01540 651324	Bothy at Ruigh Aiteachain No cutting of live timber please
13/k	MAR LODGE ESTATE * National Trust for Scotland 5 Charlotte Square Edinburgh EH2 4DU	Ranger Service Stable Block Mar Lodge Estate Braemar Aberdeenshire Tel 013397 41669	
13/m	INVERCAULD* Invercauld Estates' Trustees c/o The Factor Estate Office The Keiloch Braemar AB35 5TR	The Factor Tel 013397 41224	For Gleann an t-Slugain park in the approach to Keiloch Genuine wild camping is not a problem but please do not camp near public roads Visitors are asked to respect lambing nesting and deer cull seasons

* East Grampian Deer Management Group Member

Estate Ref	Estate Name	Contact	Estate Requests
13/n	MAR ESTATE* Proprietors of Mar Estate per Savills 12 Clerk Street Brechin DD9 6AE	I J Campbell Head Stalker Pinewood Inverey Braemar Tel 013397 41368	
14/a	PHONES ETTERIDGE AND CUAICH The Hon M Samuel per Finlayson Hughes 45 Church Street Inverness IV1 1DR	Head Keeper Tel 01540 673568	Estate carries out deer culling between mid-Sept and 20 Oct Please avoid these dates if possible unless contact has been made with the estate
14/b	GAICK Gaick Estates Ltd Gaick Lodge Kingussie	Mr Phillip Cairney Head Keeper Tel 01540 661095	
14/c	GLENFESHIE Will Woodlands per West Highland Estates Office 33 High Street Fort William PH33 6DJ	A Dempster Head Stalker Glen Feshie Kincraig Tel 01540 651324	Bothy at Ruigh Aiteachain No cutting of live timber please
14/d	MAR LODGE ESTATE * National Trust for Scotland 5 Charlotte Square Edinburgh EH2 4DU	Ranger Service Stable Block Mar Lodge Estate Braemar Aberdeenshire Tel 013397 41669	
14/e	NORTH AND SOUTH DRUMOCHTER Mrs J Drysdale Ralia Newtonmore Inverness-shire PH20 1BE	Brian Troup North Drumochter Dalwhinnie Tel 01528 522291	
14/f	DALNACARDOCH** Savills Royal British House Leonard Street Perth PH2 8HA	Keeper Ben Fernie Tel 01796 483223 or Savills Tel 01738 445588	

East Grampian Deer Management Group Member
** East Loch Ericht Deer Management Group Member

Estate Ref	Estate Name	Contact	Estate Requests
14/g	ATHOLL per The Factor Atholl Estates Office Blair Atholl Perthshire	Tel 01796 481355	Camping only at designated sites at Falls of Tarf GR983797 and Gilbert's Bridge GR881699 Vehicle access no longer available in Glen Tilt Please use car park provided Due to grouse shooting and stalking please use signed routes between 12 Aug and 20 Oct unless contact has been made with the estate
14/h	FEALAR Spearman Trustees per Atholl Estates Estates Office Blair Atholl Perthshire	The Factor Atholl Estates Office Tel 01796 481355	No cars Due to grouse shooting and stalking access between 12 August and 20 October by prior arrangement with the estate factor
14/i	CORRIEVARKIE**	John Duncan Stalker Tel 01882 633246 or 01831 213339 (the second number is a mobile number)	
14/k	TALLADH-A-BHEITH ** Adrian J M Van Well per A F Barton Lowther Scott-Harden Melville Square Comrie Perthshire PH6 2DL	Bobby Robertson Ardlarach Farm Rannoch Pitlochry Perthshire PH17 2QP Tel 01882 633220	
14/m	CRAIGANOUR** Astel Ltd per Savills Royal British House Leonard Street Perth PH2 8HA	H Littlejohn Craiganour Lodge Kinloch Rannoch Pitlochry Perthshire Tel 01882 632324	

** *East Loch Ericht Deer Management Group Member*

Estate Ref	Estate Name	Contact	Estate Requests
14/n	DALNASPIDAL** B R Adams Dalnaspidal Lodge Calvine By Pitlochry Perthshire	John Kennedy Stalker Old Schoolhouse Dalnaspidal Tel 01796 483204	Parking at Dalnaspidal Station or in lay-by on A9
14/o	DUNALASTAIR** Ian de Sales La Terrière Dunalastair Estate by Pitlochry Perthshire PH16 5PD	Keeper Tel 01882 632320 or Lochgarry House Tel 01882 632314	Approach from B847 Kinloch Rannoch/ Trinafour Road Grid Ref 712621
14/p	FOREST ENTERPRISE Inverpark Dunkeld Perthshire PH8 0JR	Tel 01350 727284/ 5	
14/q	LUDE A D Gordon Lude Steading Blair Atholl Perthshire	Keeper Alistair Stephen Tel 01796 481460	Please use camp sites in Blair Atholl and use signed routes during the shooting season 12 Aug - 20 Oct unless contact has been made with the estate
14/r	GLENFERNATE David Heathcoat-Amory MP Glenfernate Enochdhu Perthshire	Head Keeper Gordon McGregor Glenfernate Tel 01250 881205	Parking at public road No cars beyond Private Sign Please contact Head Keeper during stalking season
14/s	URRARD Andrew Mackinnon Urrard Killiecrankie Pitlochry Perthshire PH16 5LN	W McLauchlan Urrard Tel 01796 473305	Dogs on leads at all times
14/t	BALEDMUND A F Fergusson Pitfourie Pitlochry Perthshire PH16 5QZ	Tel 01796 473434	Use sign-posted car park Keep dogs on lead or to heel

* East Loch Ericht Deer Management Group Member

Estate Ref	Estate Name	Contact	Estate Requests
15/a	FEALAR Spearman Trustees per Atholl Estates Estates Office Blair Atholl Perthshire	The Factor Atholl Estates Office Tel 01796 481355	No cars Due to grouse shooting and stalking access between 12 August and 20 October by prior arrangement with the estate factor
15/b	DALMUNZIE Dalmunzie Ltd Spittal of Glenshee Blairgowrie Perthshire PH10 7QG	Simon Winton c/o Dalmunzie Hotel Tel 01250 885226	Please telephone for access information during stalking season £2 for parking at hotel
15/c	INVERCAULD (land outwith EGDMG area)	Information below	
15/d/1	INVERCAULD* Invercauld Estates' Trustees c/o The Factor Estate Office The Keiloch Braemar AB35 5TR	The Factor Tel 013397 41224	For Gleann an t-Slugain park in the approach to Keiloch Genuine wild camping is not a problem but please do not camp near public roads Visitors are asked to respect lambing nesting and deer cull seasons
15/d/2	MAR ESTATE* Proprietors of Mar Estate per Savills 12 Clerk Street Brechin DD9 6AE	I J Campbell Head Stalker Pinewood Inverey Braemar Tel 013397 41368	
15/d/3	MAR LODGE ESTATE* National Trust for Scotland 5 Charlotte Square Edinburgh EH2 4DU	Ranger Service Stable Block Mar Lodge Estate Braemar Aberdeenshire Tel 013397 41669	

East Grampian Deer Management Group Member

Estate Ref	Estate Name	Contact	Estate Requests
15/d/4	BALMORAL* The Balmoral Estates' Trustees The Estates Office Balmoral Ballater Aberdeenshire AB35 5TB	The Factor The Estates Office Tel 013397 42334/5 Countryside Ranger Tel 013397 55434	Ranger/ Naturalist service at Spittal of Glenmuick provides full access information
15/d/5	GLENMUICK* per Savills 12 Clerk Street Brechin Angus DD9 6AE	A Taylor Head Keeper's House Glen Muick Tel 013397 55403	
15/d/6	GLEN TANAR ESTATE* Glen Tanar Estate Brooks House Glen Tanar Aboyne AB34 5EU Tel 013398 86451 Fax 013398 86047	Glen Tanar Charitable Trust Ranger Service Braeloine Centre Glen Tanar Aboyne AB34 5EU Tel 013398 86072	
15/d/7	INVERMARK* per The Factor Dalhousie Estates Office Brechin DD9 6EL	F Taylor Head Keeper Kirkton of Invermark Glen Esk by Brechin Tel 01356 670208	Public car park at Invermark Camping only at Tarfside Field GR493795 Please ask at shop
15/d/8	HUNTHILL* per The Factor Dalhousie Estates Office Brechin DD9 6EL	D Wilson Head Keeper Head Keeper's House Glen Lethnot by Brechin Tel 01356 660295	
15/d/9	MILLDEN* per The Factor Dalhousie Estates Office Brechin DD9 6EL	D Caithness Head Keeper's House Millden Glen Esk Brechin Tel 01356 670267	
15/d/10	GLENDYE* Fasque Estate Office Laurencekirk Kincardineshire AB30 1DJ	A S Wallace Factor Tel 01561 340202 or A Dykes Head Keeper The Kennels Glen Dye Tel 01330 850656	

East Grampian Deer Management Group Member

Estate Ref	Estate Name	Contact	Estate Requests
15/d/11	DINNET* Dinnet & Kinord Estates Estate Office Dinnet Aboyne AB34 5LL	D Fraser North Lodge Dinnet Aboyne Tel 013398 85259	
15/d/12	AIRLIE* per Airlie Estate Office Cortachy Kirriemuir Angus DD8 4LY	A Mearns Rottal Lodge Cottage Glen Clova Tel 01575 550230	
15/d/13	GLENPROSEN* Trustees of the Glenprosen Settlement per West Highland Estates Office 21 Argyll Square Oban PA34 4AT	A Boath Craig Lodge Cottage Glen Prosen Kirriemuir Tel 01575 540314	
15/d/14	TULCHAN* Tulchan of Glenisla Forest Ltd c/o Youngs Manor Street Forfar DD8 1EX	The Factor Youngs Chartered Surveyors Tel 01307 462516 R Smith Head Stalker Tel 01575 582321	
16/a	DELL per Messrs Bowlts Chartered Surveyors Barnhill Pluscarden By Elgin Moray IV30 3TZ	Messrs Bowlts Chartered Surveyors Barnhill Pluscarden By Elgin Moray IV30 3TZ Tel 01343 890400 Fax 01343 890222	
16/b	KILLIN Killin Estate Killin Inverness-shire	Tel 01456 486660	
16/c	GARROGIE Charles R Connell Garrogie Whitebridge Inverness-shire IV1 2UR	Stalker Tel 01456 486254	

* East Grampian Deer Management Group Member

Estate Ref	Estate Name	Contact	Estate Requests
16/d	CORRIEGARTH per Finlayson Hughes 29 Barossa Place Perth PH1 5EP	Mr W Johnston Keeper's Cottage Corriegarth Gorthleck Inverness-shire Tel 01456 486374	
16/e	COIGNAFEARN Coignafearn Estate Co Ltd 8 Ardross Terrace Inverness IV3 5NW	Head Stalker Frank Stuart Tel 01808 531218	Visitors are asked not to park on the public road and to respect estate needs in shooting and stalking season and during grouse nesting and deer feeding
16/f	PITMAIN Lucas Aardenburg Pitmain Lodge Kingussie Inverness-shire	Mr W Dey Keeper's House Kingussie Tel 01540 661237	Estate huts at Dulnain and Corrour available for emergency use
16/g	GLENDOE G E M Vernon H R M Vernon per G Watson Glendoe Estate Fort Augustus Inverness-shire	Tel 01320 366234	
16/h	STRONELAIRG Charles R Connell Garrogie Whitebridge Inverness-shire IV1 2UR	Stalker Tel 01456 486254	
16/i	ARDACHY G E M Vernon H R M Vernon per G Watson Glendoe Estate Fort Augustus Inverness-shire	Tel 01320 366234	

Estate Ref	Estate Name	Contact	Estate Requests
16/k	CULACHY H G Biggs Tarff House Culachy Fort Augustus PH32 4BY	Keeper's Cottage Culachy Tel 01320 366732	Parking on public road only Please use "Wade's Road" pedestrian right of way during deer culling season 1 Aug - 1 Feb unless an alternative has been agreed
16/m	ABERCHALDER Miss Jean Ellice Taigh-an-Lianach Aberchalder Farm Invergarry PH35 4HN	Miss Jean Ellice Tel 01809 501287	Parking by prior arrangement only
16/n	BRAEROY Mr B K D Buckle Dairy Farm Office Semer Ipswich Suffolk IP7 6RA	The Stalker Braeroy Roybridge Tel 01397 712210 or 01397 712887 (Home)	Parking in lay-by close to footbridge in Glen Roy
16/o	GLENSHIRRA & SHERAMORE Alcan Highland Estates Ltd per West Highland Estates Office 33 High Street Fort William Inverness-shire PH33 6DJ	Head Stalker Tel 01528 544222	Walkers are welcome at most times and are requested to remain on rights of way during the period mid-August to mid October unless an alternative has been agreed with the head stalker
16/p	FOREST ENTERPRISE Torlundy Fort William PH33 6SW	Tel 01397 702814	
16/q	DALCHULLY Laggan Newtonmore PH20 1BU	Mrs J Ramsden Tel 01528 544270	No dogs either on or off leads at any time Stalking takes place from the last week in September until 20 October Contact is essential during this period

Estate Ref	Estate Name	Contact	Estate Requests
16/r	BLARAGIE Laggan Newtonmore Inverness-shire PH20 1AJ	Mr D J Wilson Blaragie Laggan Tel 01528 544229	No dogs either on or off leads at any time Stalking takes place from the last week in September until 20 October Contact is essential during this period
16/s	CLUNY Cluny Castle Laggan Newtonmore Inverness-shire PH20 1BS	Head Keeper Ian Sharp Tel 01528 544262	Stalking last week of Sept - 20 Oct Contact essential then No dogs during stalking and otherwise at heel or on lead No mountain bikes
16/t	GLENBANCHOR Avionholding SpA per Strutt & Parker St Nicholas House 68 Station Road Banchory Kincardineshire AB31 3YJ	Colin Niven Keeper's Cottage Glen Road Newtonmore Tel 01540 673606	Parking on glen road beside Private sign No vehicles past this point please
16/u	GLENSPEAN Mrs E J Macdonald Ardslignish Ardnamurchan Argyll PH36 4JG	Mrs E J Macdonald Tel 01972 500700	
16/v	TULLOCH Eastaff Estates Limited Roybridge Inverness-shire PH31 4AR	Estate Manager David MacDonald Tel 01397 732217	Between 1 September and 20 October Mr MacDonald will suggest a route to Beinn a' Chaorainn No dogs due to sheep worrying and killing on Beinn a' Chaorainn also west side of Creag Meagaidh
16/w	CREAG MEAGAIDH NNR Scottish Natural Heritage Achantoul Aviemore Inverness-shire PH22 1QD	Edwin Cross SNH Creag Meagaidh NNR Aberarder Kinlochlaggan Inverness-shire Tel 01528 544265 (day) 01528 544214 (evening)	The public are welcome to visit the National Nature Reserve at all times Please read signs and abide by their requests As this is a NNR no dogs allowed at any time

Estate Ref	Estate Name	Contact	Estate Requests
17/a	FOREST ENTERPRISE Torlundy Fort William PH33 6SW	Tel 01397 702184	
17/b	KILLIECHONATE WOODLANDS T I & Dowty Pensions Ltd per Tilhill Economic Forestry Old Hydro Buildings Bank Street Fort William PH33 6AY	Miller Harris Tilhill Economic Forestry Old Hydro Building Bank Street Fort William PH33 6AY Tel 01397 705101	
17/c	ARDVERIKIE Ardverikie Estates Ltd Kinlochlaggan Newtonmore Inverness-shire PH20 1BX	A J G Gibson Factor Estate Office Kinlochlaggan Tel 01528 544300	The estate welcomes considerate visitors Please telephone for further information
17/d	BEN ALDER ESTATE per Smiths Gore 7 The Square Fochabers Moray IV32 7DG	Ian Crichton Head Stalker North Lodge Ben Alder Estate Dalwhinnie Tel 01540 672000	Keys can be had from Mr Crichton to get cars to Loch Pattack Estate is not liable for damage to cars
17/e	KILLIECHONATE & MAMORE Alcan Highland Estates Ltd per West Highland Estates Office 33 High Street Fort William Inverness-shire PH33 6DJ	West Highland Estates Office 33 High Street Fort William Tel 01397 702433 Mamore Stalker Tel 01855 831337 Killiechonate Stalker Tel 01397 712547	Walkers are welcome at most times and are requested to remain on rights of way or high ridges during the period mid-August to mid-October unless an alternative has been agreed with the stalker for the appropriate area
17/f	CORROUR Corrour Estate Ltd per Strutt & Parker St Nicholas House 68 Station Road Banchory Kincardineshire AB31 3YJ	Ted Piggott Head Stalker Corrour Estate Tel 01397 732200	No vehicles allowed on the Estate Parking on A86 Please use paths when possible and confirm routes in advance with Head Stalker during stalking season

Estate Ref	Estate Name	Contact	Estate Requests
17/g	DUNAN Hamish McCorquodale Dunan Lodge Rannoch Station Pitlochry Perthshire PH17 2QD Tel 01882 633230	Colin Robertson Dunan Lodge Rannoch Station Pitlochry Perthshire PH17 2QD Tel 01882 633266	
17/h	CAMUSERICHT Camusericht Lodge Bridge of Gaur Rannoch Station Perthshire PH17 2QP	G A Macdonald Bridge of Ericht Tel 01882 633268 or 01882 633207 (answering machine)	During the stalking season it is essential to contact the estate when approaching either Ben Alder or Ben Alder cottage from the west or the south
17/i	BLACK CORRIES Vicomte Adolphe de Spoelberch per West Highland Estates Office 21 Argyll Square Oban PA34 4AT	Peter O'Connell Black Corries Estate Tel 01855 851272	No parking on road between Kingshouse and Lodge Please use stiles Stalking and culling takes place between September and 15 February In the interests of safety it is essential to make contact before going on the hill
17/k	RANNOCH DEER MANAGEMENT ASSOCIATION Rannoch Barracks by Rannoch Station	Nicholas Thexton Gaur Cottage by Rannoch Station Tel 01882 633248	
17/m	GLENCOE & DALNESS National Trust for Scotland 5 Charlotte Square Edinburgh EH2 4DU	The Ranger Achnacon House Glencoe Tel 01855 811729	
18T/a	FOREST ENTERPRISE Millpark Road Oban Argyll PA34 4NH	Tel 01631 566155	
18T/b	GLENLEACNAMUIDHE	Mr W Elliott Achnabeidh Glencoe Argyll Tel 01855 811311	

Estate Ref	Estate Name	Contact	Estate Requests
18T/c	GLENCOE & DALNESS National Trust for Scotland 5 Charlotte Square Edinburgh EH2 4DU	The Ranger Achnacon House Tel 01855 811729	
18T/d	GLENCRERAN SAC Advisory Office Glencruitten Road Oban Argyll PA34 4DW	Mr G Livingstone Stalker Cottage Glencreran Appin Tel 01631 730312	New deer fence at Drimavuaic round woodland regeneration area For access to hill use gate between Drimavuaic House access and lay-by
18T/e	GLEN ETIVE Mr Robin Fleming Black Mount Bridge of Orchy Argyll	Angus Smith Tel 01855 851277	All dogs on leads please When possible please use paths and ridges To assist with stag cull please leave hills quiet in September and first half of October.
18T/f	DALNESS ESTATE Mr R J Fleming per Strutt & Parker St Nicholas House 68 Station Road Banchory Kincardineshire AB31 3YJ	Alastair Hunter Dalness Tel 01855 851252	No vehicle access
18T/g	BLACKMOUNT Mr Robin Fleming Black Mount Bridge of Orchy Argyll	Hamish Menzies Tel 01838 400225 or Ian MacRae Tel 01838 400269	Parking at Victoria Bridge All dogs on leads please When possible please use paths and ridges To assist with stag cull please leave hills quiet in September and first half of October
18T/h	ARDCHATTAN Mrs James Troughton Ardchattan Priory Connel Argyll	Malcolm MacDonald Ardachy Farm Ardchattan Tel 01631 710274	Please leave hills quiet between 15 Sept-15 Oct to assist with stag cull

Estate Ref	Estate Name	Contact	Estate Requests
18T/i 18B/a	GLENKINGLASS The Hon Mrs L F Schuster & The Hon Mrs D C Fleming per West Highland Estates Office 21 Argyll Square Oban PA34 4AT Tel 01631 563617	Tim Healy Stalker Ardmaddy Taynuilt Argyll Tel 01866 822271	No vehicular access
18B/b	GLENOE Mr Lewis Heriot Maitland per Mr Ian Stewart Invernoe Loch Etive Taynuilt Argyll PA35 1JT	Mr Ian Stewart Tel 01866 822212 Fax 01866 822578	
18B/c	CASTLES ESTATE E Smith & Sons		No dogs either on or off leads at any time Please avoid estate during part of stalking season 20 Sept - 20 Oct Take note of the signs which are posted daily
18B/d	GLENSTRAE DUILETTER/ CRUACHAN Mr Richard Schuster Glenstrae Dalmally Argyll PA33 1AP	Derek Dempster Duiletter Bungalow Tel 01838 200217 Andrew Servant Straebridge Cottage Tel 01838 200492	
18B/e	FOREST ENTERPRISE Millpark Road Oban Argyll PA34 4NH	Tel 01631 566155	
18B/f	AUCH Lord Trevor Auch Lodge Bridge of Orchy Argyll	C Macdonald Fir Park Bridge of Orchy Argyll Tel 01839 400233	Please keep dogs on leads at all times and try to avoid Sept to 20 Oct and lambing time unless contact has been made

Estate Ref	Estate Name	Contact	Estate Requests
18B/g	TILHILL ECONOMIC FORESTRY Claremont Glencruitten Road Oban Argyll PA34 4QA	District Manager Tilhill Economic Forestry Tel 01631 562906	
18B/h	ARGYLL Trustees of the Tenth Duke of Argyll Argyll Office Cherry Park Inveraray	The Factor Argyll Estates Office Inveraray Tel 01499 302203	Park at locked gate in Glen Shira
18B/i	ARDKINGLAS Mr John Noble Ardkinglas House Cairndow Argyll	Ardkinglas Estate Office Cairndow Argyll Tel 01499 600621	Access up Glen Fyne on foot only Park cars on A83 Avoid lambing and stalking seasons
18B/k	GLENFALLOCH F A Richardson & Others Glenfalloch Lodge Ardlui	F Frost Clisham Cottage Glen Falloch Tel 01301 704229	Camping at Ben Glas Farm for walkers only No cars Tel 01301 704281
18B/m	BEN LUI NATIONAL NATURE RESERVE Scottish Natural Heritage	SNH Area Officer (Lorn) Glensalloch Road Barcaldine Oban PA37 1SF Tel 01631 720363	Access up Cononish Glen on foot only
18B/n	FOREST ENTERPRISE Whitegates Lochgilphead Argyll PA31 8RS	Tel 01546 602518	
19/a	BLACKMOUNT* Mr Robin Fleming Black Mount Bridge of Orchy Argyll	Hamish Menzies Tel 01838 400225 or Ian Macrae Tel 01838 400269	Parking at Achallader Farm All dogs on leads please When possible please use paths and ridges To assist with stag cull please leave hills quiet in September and first half of October

West Rannoch Deer Management Group Member

Estate Ref	Estate Name	Contact	Estate Requests
19/b	LOCHS* Lochs Estate Glen Lyon Aberfeldy	W Mason Croc-na-Keys Lochs Estate Glen Lyon Aberfeldy Tel 01887 866224	
19/c	MEGGERNIE* Meggernie Estate Bridge of Balgie Aberfeldy	G Grant Keeper's Cottage Bridge of Balgie Aberfeldy Tel 01887 866247	
19/d	AUCH* Lord Trevor Auch Lodge Bridge of Orchy Argyll	C Macdonald Fir Park Bridge of Orchy Argyll Tel 01839 400233	Please keep dogs on leads at all times and try to avoid Sept to 20 Oct and lambing time unless contact has been made
19/e	INVERMEARAN* Clemens Hoss Pubil Lodge Glen Lyon Aberfeldy PH15 2PX	Neil Mackay Grianan Cottage Invermearan Estate Glen Lyon Aberfeldy PH15 2PX Tel 01887 866225	
19/f	CASHLIE* W H Porter Cashlie Estate Bridge of Balgie Aberfeldy PH15 2PP	D Sinclair Keeper Cashlie Estate Bridge of Balgie Aberfeldy PH15 2PP Tel 01887 866237	Please keep dogs on leads Walkers are welcome but have a word at the stalker's cottage during September and October
19/g	GLEN LOCHAY John B Cameron Balbuthie Leven Fife KY9 1EX	Farm Manager Kenknock Glen Lochay Killin Perthshire FK21 8UB Tel 01567 820278	All dogs on leads please

* West Rannoch Deer Management Group Member

Estate Ref	Estate Name	Contact	Estate Requests
19/h	BORELAND* Judge R A R Stroyan QC Boreland Killin Perthshire FK21 8TT	T Frost Kennels Cottage Boreland Estate Killin FK21 8UA Tel 01567 820562	Please avoid ground between Meall Glas and Meall nan Tarmachan during stalking season unless contact is made with the estate
19/i	MORENISH* Mr H J Sants Court Farm Worminghall Nr Aylesbury Bucks HP18 8LD	J Sinclair Tirai Craignavie Road Killin Tel 01567 820553	
19/k	FOREST ENTERPRISE Millpark Road Oban PA34 4NH	Tel 01631 566155	
19/m	LOCHDOCHART W J Christie of Loch Dochart OBE Lochdochart Crianlarich FK20 8QS	Hamish MacLaughlin or Derek Christie Tel 01838 300275 or 01838 300295	
19/n	AUCHESSAN* A W Cory-Wright Auchessan Estate Crianlarich Perthshire FK20 8QS	D Cannon Shepherd's House Auchessan Crianlarich Tel 01567 820518	No off-road parking except in public lay-bys on A85 Please be sure to close all gates No dogs even on leads Please phone to check during stalking season
19/q	BENMORE FARM Fulton C Ronald Keilator Farm Crianlarich Perthshire FK20 8RL	Fulton C Ronald Tel 01838 300281 or 01838 300287	No dogs allowed at any time even on a lead Please exercise care during the lambing season 25 April to 25 May

West Rannoch Deer Management Group Member

Estate Ref	Estate Name	Contact	Estate Requests
19/o	AUCHLYNE & SUIE* Mrs E Paterson & Mrs J Bowser Auchlyne Killin Perthshire FK21 8RG	George Coyne Keeper's Cottage Auchlyne Killin FK21 8RG Tel 01567 820487	Parking in lay-bys on A85 for Ben More Please keep to ridges Please do not park between Barncroft and Auchlyne Farm for Sgiath Chuil/ Meall a' Churain Please keep dogs on leads at all times and try to avoid Estate 1 Sept to 20 Oct unless contact is made
19/p	GLENFALLOCH F A Richardson & Others Glenfalloch Lodge Ardlui	F Frost Clisham Cottage Glen Falloch Tel 01301 704229	Camping at Ben Glas Farm for walkers only No cars Tel 01301 704281
19/r	INVERLOCHLARIG Braes Farming Co Inverlochlarig Balquhidder Lochearnhead	J or M McNaughton Inverlochlarig Tel 01877 384232 or 384239	Parking/ picnic area provided by Braes Farming Co No dogs during lambing time please Please inquire at farm or telephone before proceeding to the hills from mid September until 20 October (stalking season)
19/s	FOREST ENTERPRISE Aberfoyle District Aberfoyle Stirling FK8 3UX	Tel 01877 382383	
19/t	BLAIRCREICH per Tilhill Economic Forestry The Estate Office Sandbank Dunoon Argyll PA23 8BN	Mr & Mrs B G Hughes Tel 01877 384231	Parking at Inverlochlarig Please do not enter deer- fenced area when shooting is in progress as notified on signs at approach road and gateway and contact re alternative routes Please no dogs or mountain bikes

West Rannoch Deer Management Group Member

Estate Ref	Estate Name	Contact	Estate Requests
19/u	MONACHYLE TUARACH	Juan Arkotxa Monachyle Tuarach Tel 01877 384671	No fires Dogs on leads
19/v	IMMEREON	W H Hendry & Sons Immereon Balquhidder Lochearnhead Perthshire FK19 8PF	No vehicular access across road end bridge Dogs must be kept on leads Please be sure to close all gates
19/w	LOCH KATRINE West of Scotland Water Authority 419 Balmore Road Glasgow G22 6NU	A Fail Stronachlachar Tel 01877 386210	Parking outwith the catchment area No camping or pollution of catchment area
19/x	GLENFINGLAS John B Cameron Balbuthie Leven Fife KY9 1EX	Farm Manager Tel 01877 376256	No camping Water catchment area Please keep all dogs on lead
19/y	MILTON OF CALLANDER Moray Estates Development Co Estates Office Forres Moray IV36 0ET	R Scott Milton of Callander Farm Callander Tel 01877 330812	Parking very limited on sides of A821 Please do not block farm entrances
20/a	FOREST ENTERPRISE areas North of Loch Tay Inverpark Dunkeld Perthshire PH8 0JR areas South of Loch Tay Aberfoyle District Aberfoyle Stirling FK8 3UX	Tel 01350 727284/5

Tel 01877 382383 | |
| 20/b | CORRIE CARIE ** M Pearson The Barracks Kinloch Rannoch | Nicholas Thexton Gaur Cottage by Rannoch Station Tel 01882 633248 | |

** East Glen Lyon Deer Management Group Member

Estate Ref	Estate Name	Contact	Estate Requests
20/c	INNERHADDEN** L Barclay Innerhadden Kinloch Rannoch	L Barclay Tel 01882 632344 or 01882 632457 or C Maclaran Tel 01882 632339	
20/d	DALCHOSNIE** Col J H C Horsfall DSO MC Dalchosnie Kinloch Rannoch by Pitlochry Perthshire PH16 5QD	Mrs Christine Wilson Braes of Foss Farm Tummel Bridge Pitlochry Tel 01887 830324	Car park is provided beside monument
20/e	WEST TEMPAR** Mrs John Dawes and Mr and Mrs Andrew Mineyko West Tempar Kinloch Rannoch PH16 5QE	W A Mineyko West Tempar House Tel 01882 632338	
20/f	CROSSMOUNT** Ian de Sales La Terrière Dunalastair Estate Pitlochry Perthshire	Keeper Tel 01882 632320 or Lochgarry House Tel 01882 632314	Please use Forest Enterprise car park at Braes of Foss
20/g	KYNACHAN** Col J H C Horsfall DSO MC Dalchosnie Kinloch Rannoch by Pitlochry Perthshire PH16 5QD	Mrs Christine Wilson Braes of Foss Farm Tummel Bridge Pitlochry Tel 01887 830324	Car park is provided beside monument
20/h	GLENGOULANDIE** H S & Mrs J E McAdam Glengoulandie Foss by Pitlochry Perthshire	H S & Mrs J E McAdam Glengoulandie Foss Tel 01887 830261	Parking in caravan site car park
20/i	GARTH** Messrs Buchan McAdam Samuels Comrie Farm Keltneyburn Aberfeldy Perthshire PH15 2LS	H McAdam Glengoulandie Tel 01887 830261	Please do not use Pheiginn Bothy

* East Glen Lyon Deer Management Group Member

Estate Ref	Estate Name	Contact	Estate Requests
20/k	INCHGARTH** R Partridge Inchgarth Keltneyburn	R Partridge Tel 01887 830534	
20/m	NORTH CHESTHILL** Trustees of Mrs I K Molteno Dr M J Riddell Dornoch Lodge Glen Lyon Aberfeldy PH15 2NH	The Trustee Tel 01887 877244 The Stalker Tel 01877 820071	Path up Carn Gorm from Invervar Smiddy preferred Tel kiosk at Invervar Smiddy can be used to make contact during stalking season
20/n	INNERWICK* Mr and Mrs R W Whewell Innerwick House Glen Lyon Aberfeldy PH15 2PP	W Drysdale Tel 01887 866218	To assist with stag cull please leave hills quiet from 22 Sept - 20 Oct
20/o	RORO* Glen Lyon Aberfeldy Perthshire PH15 2PW	Donald Campbell Tel 01887 866216	
20/p	INVERINAIN* Estate Office Bughtrig Coldstream Berwickshire TD12 4JP	H Shearer Tel 01887 877233	
20/q	SOUTH CHESTHILL* Estate Office Bughtrig Coldstream Berwickshire TD12 4JP	H Shearer Tel 01887 877233	
20/r	CULDAREMORE** Culdaremore Ltd Culdaremore Fortingall Glen Lyon	Farm Manager Tel 01887 830394	
20/s	BEN LAWERS* National Trust for Scotland 5 Charlotte Square Edinburgh EH2 4DU	The Ranger NTS Visitor Centre Killin Tel 01567 820397 or 820988	Please take care to avoid damage to plants in the high corries and wet flushes

** East Glen Lyon Deer Management Group Member
* West Rannoch Deer Management Group Member

Estate Ref	Estate Name	Contact	Estate Requests
20/t	WESTER TULLICH Ardeonaig Killin	Shepherd Tel 01567 820410	
20/u	ARDTALNAIG	Mr R Hannigan Easter Moncrieffe Bridge of Earn Perth PH2 8QA	Please avoid damage to young trees in areas of regeneration Please keep dogs on leads Please do not leave empty bottles
20/v	REMONY Aberfeldy Perthshire PH15 2HR	Mr J Duncan Millar Tel 01887 830209	
20/w	AUCHNAFREE J J I Whitaker Auchnafree Lodge Amulree Dunkeld Perthshire PH8 0EH	The Keeper Tel 01350 725285	
20/x	INVERGELDIE James F Priestley Cottage D Headbourne Worthy House Winchester Hampshire SO23 7JG	Tel 01764 670959 or 670240	
20/y	DRUMMOND ESTATES Glenartney & Lochearnside Drummond Estates Estate Office Muthill Perthshire PH5 2AA	A Work Auchinner Glenartney Tel 01764 670733 J Anderson Woodend Lochearnhead Tel 01567 830329 Estate Office Tel 01764 681257	
20/z	GLEN TURRET Glen Turret Estates Ltd	Lawers Estate Co Ltd Lawers House Comrie Perthshire PH6 2LT Tel 01764 670050	

Estate Ref	Estate Name	Contact	Estate Requests
20/az	GLENAMPLE ESTATE per Strutt & Parker St Nicholas House 68 Station Road Banchory Kincardineshire AB31 3YJ	M Holliday Head Stalker Glenample Estate Tel 01567 830344	Please agree a route with the Head Stalker during the stalking season
20/bz	ARDVORLICH Mr Alexander Stewart Ardvorlich Lochearnhead Perthshire FK19 8QE	Estate Keeper Findoglen St Fillans Perthshire Tel 01764 685260	Please avoid first three weeks of October if at all possible Dogs on leads at all times please Cars should be left beside public road
21T/a	STUCKINDROIN	Tel 01301 704283	Please take care during lambing No dogs please
21T/b	STRONE ESTATE	Mr J M Turnbull Tel 01499 600284	
21T/c	SLOY Scottish Hydro Electric plc 10 Dunkeld Road Perth PH2 5WA	Hydro Headquarters Clunie Power Station Pitlochry Perthshire PH16 5NF	Please do not park cars at the entrance to the Loch Sloy road 24 hour access required Use car park at viewpoint in front of Sloy Power Station
21T/d	INVERUGLAS J B & I Duncan Inveruglas	Tel 01301 704210	Use car park in front of Sloy Power Station Please take care during lambing mid-April to mid-May No dogs please
21T/e	GLENCROE Sqn Ldr A Davidson Coilessan House Ardgartan Arrochar G83 7AR	Glencroe Farm Tel 01301 702523	Please cross hill fences only at the stiles provided Camping by prior permission only Hill livestock grazing - no dogs
21T/f	ARGYLL FOREST PARK Forest Enterprise Kilmun by Dunoon Argyll PA23 8SE	Tel 01369 840666	

Estate Ref	Estate Name	Contact	Estate Requests
21T/g	FOREST ENTERPRISE Aberfoyle District Aberfoyle Stirling FK8 3UX	Tel 01877 382383	
21T/h	BEN LOMOND National Trust for Scotland 5 Charlotte Square Edinburgh EH2 4DU	The Ranger Ardess Lodge Rowardennan Tel 01360 870224	
21B/a	DOUGARIE The Estate Office Dougarie Isle of Arran KA27 8EB Tel 01770 840259	Head Stalker The Towers Dougarie Tel 01770 840224	
21B/b	ARRAN & SANNOX The Estate Office Brodick Isle of Arran	Arran Estate Office Tel 01770 302203 (9am-5pm) The Head Stalker Tel 01770 302223 (evenings)	
21B/c	GOATFELL & GLEN ROSA National Trust for Scotland 5 Charlotte Square Edinburgh EH2 4DU	The Ranger Brodick Castle Tel 01770 302462	Car park at Brodick Castle
21B/d	FOREST ENTERPRISE Brodick Isle of Arran	Tel 01770 302218	
22/a	FOREST ENTERPRISE Forest Enterprise Castle Douglas Forest District 21 King Street Castle Douglas DG7 1AA	Tel 01556 503626	
22/b	GALLOWAY FOREST PARK Forest Enterprise as for 22/a above	Tel as above for 22/a	

Estate Ref	Estate Name	Contact	Estate Requests
22/c	GARROCH J N Roper-Caldbeck Dunveoch New Galloway Castle Douglas	J N Roper-Caldbeck Tel 01644 430381	The Southern Upland Way crosses the estate over Drumbuie and Clenrie Farms
22/d	FORREST ESTATE Dalry Castle Douglas DG7 3XS	Estate Office Forrest Estate Tel 01644 430230	Please use car parks provided
22/e	TILHILL ECONOMIC FORESTRY The Old School Crossmichael Castle Douglas	Tel 01556 670301	
23/a	FOREST ENTERPRISE Ae Forest District Ae Village Parkgate Dumfries DG1 1QB	Tel 01387 860247/8	
23/b	CULTER ALLERS McCosh Brothers	Gerard McCosh Tel 01899 220410	
23/c	STANHOPE ESTATE Broughton ML12 6QJ	The Manager The Old Hostel Tel 01899 880257	Electric fences in operation Parking on main road only
23/d	WEMYSS & MARCH ESTATE Lord Wemyss Trust Estates Office Longniddry East Lothian EH32 OPY	For Hart Fell and White Coomb Norman Douglas Farm Manager Catslackburn Yarrow Tel 01750 82206 For Ettrick Hills Mr Pringle Riskinhope Farm Tel 01750 42207	Leave cars at Winterhopeburn at Shepherd's house This route is part of the Southern Upland Way
23/e	TILHILL ECONOMIC FORESTRY Forestry House Well Road Moffat Dumfries-shire DG10 9AU	Tel 01683 220372	Please use contact number in times of high fire risk

Estate Ref	Estate Name	Contact	Estate Requests
23/f	GREY MARE'S TAIL WHITE COOMB & LOCH SKEEN National Trust for Scotland 5 Charlotte Square Edinburgh EH2 4DU	Chief Ranger National Trust for Scotland 5 Charlotte Square Edinburgh EH2 4DU Tel 0131 2265922	Seasonal Ranger in July/ August only
23/g	QUEENSBERRY ESTATE The Buccleuch Estates Ltd Drumlanrig Mains Thornhill Dumfries-shire DG3 4AG	The Factor Mr N Waugh Tel 01848 600283	Contact Estate Office re any over-night camping
24/a	LOCHURD W A B Noble Lochurd West Linton Peebles-shire	W A B Noble Lochurd Tel 01899 860244	Fences are either all electrified or have electric scare wires so please use gates and close them behind you
24/b	CULTER ALLERS McCosh Brothers	Gerard McCosh Tel 01899 220410	
24/c	STANHOPE ESTATE Broughton ML12 6QJ	The Manager The Old Hostel Tel 01899 880257	Electric fences in operation Parking on main road only
24/d	WEMYSS & MARCH ESTATE Lord Wemyss Trust Estates Office Longniddry East Lothian EH32 0PY	For Black Law J Mitchell Tel 01750 42244 For Broad Law and Cramalt Craig Farm Manager Tel 01750 82206 or Shepherd Meggethead Tel 01750 42236	Leave cars at Meggethead
24/e	TILHILL ECONOMIC FORESTRY Forestry House Well Road Moffat Dumfries-shire DG10 9AU	Tel 01683 220372	Please use contact number in times of high fire risk

INDEX OF MOUNTAINS AND OTHER AREAS REFERRED TO IN THE TEXT

Mountain or Mountain Group	Map	Mountain or Mountain Group	Map
Ben Klibreck	3A	Bidean nam Bian Group	18T
Beinn Lair	5	Bidein a' Choire Sheasgaich	6
Beinn na Lap	17	Binnein Shuas	17
Ben Lawers Group	20	Braeriach	13
Ben Ledi	19	Braigh nan Uamhachan	9
Beinn Leoid	2	Breabag	2
Beinn Liath Mhor	6	Broad Cairn	15
Ben Lomond	21T	Broad Law	24
Ben Loyal	1	Broughton Heights	24
Ben Lui Group	18B	Buachaille Etive Beag	18T
Ben Macdui	13	Buachaille Etive Mor	18T
Beinn Mhanach	19	Buidhe Bheinn	8T
Beinn Mheadhonach	14	Bynack More	13
Beinn Mhic-Mhonaidh	18B		
Beinn Mhic Cedidh	9	Cairn Bannoch	15
Beinn Mholach	14	Cairn Gorm	13
Beinn Mhor (Harris)	10T	Cairn of Claise	15
Beinn a' Mhuinidh	5	Cairnsmore of Carsphairn	22
Ben More (Crianlarich)	19	Cairnsmore of Fleet	22
Ben More Assynt	2	Cairn Toul	13
Ben Mor Coigach	2	Canisp	2
Beinn na Caillich	8T	Carn a' Choire Ghairbh	7B
Beinn na h-Eaglaise	8T	Carn a' Chlamain	14
Beinn nan Caorach	8T	Carn a' Chuilinn	16
Beinn nan Imirean	19	Carn Ban	4
Beinn nan Oighreag	19	Carn Bhac	15
Ben Nevis	17	Carn na Caim	14
Beinn Odhar Bheag	9	Carn Chuinneag	4
Ben Pharlagain	17	Carn Dearg (Glen Roy)	8B
Beinn Resipol	9	Carn Dearg (Loch Ossian)	17
Beinn Sgritheall	8T	Carn Easgann Bana	16
Beinn Sgulaird	18T	Carn Eighe	7B
Beinn Spionnaidh	1	Carn an Fhidhleir	14
Ben Stack	1	Carn Ghluasaid	7B
Ben Starav	18T	Carn Gorm	7T
Beinn Tarsuinn	5	Carn Gorm (Glen Lyon)	20
Beinn Teallach	16	Carn Liath	16
Ben Tee	8B	Carn Mairg	20
Beinn Tharsuinn	6	Carn Mor	8T
Ben Tirran	15	Carn an Righ	15
Beinn Trilleachan	18T	Carn an t-Sagairt Mor	15
Beinn Tulaichean	19	Chno Dearg	17
Beinn Udlaidh	18B	Ciste Dhubh Group	7B
Beinn Udlamain	14	Clach Leathad	18T
Benvane	19	Clisham	10T
Ben Venue	19	Conival	2
Ben Vorlich (Loch Earn)	20	Corrieyairack Hill	16
Ben Vorlich (Loch Lomond)	21T	Cramalt Craig	24
Ben Vrackie	14	Cranstackie	1
Ben Wyvis	4	Creach Bheinn	18T
		Creagan na Beinne	20

NOTES

NOTES

NOTES

NOTES

NOTES

NOTES

NOTES